# FOR THE LOVE OF
# RADIO 4

## THE UNOFFICIAL PUZZLE BOOK

### NEIL SOMERVILLE

summersdale

FOR THE LOVE OF RADIO 4: THE UNOFFICIAL PUZZLE BOOK

An Hachette UK Company
www.hachette.co.uk

Summersdale Publishers Ltd
Part of Octopus Publishing Group Limited
Carmelite House
50 Victoria Embankment
LONDON
EC4Y 0DZ
UK

www.summersdale.com

Printed and bound in Poland

ISBN: 978-1-78783-566-5

Substantial discounts on bulk quantities of Summersdale books are available to corporations, professional associations and other organizations. For details contact general enquiries by telephone: +44 (0) 1243 771107 or email: enquiries@summersdale.com.

*This book is dedicated to you*
*as a thank you for your interest.*

# INTRODUCTION

Radio 4 is a cornucopia of delights. Whether it's keeping listeners informed of the latest news developments, airing the views of experts or entertaining us with drama, music, quizzes and much more besides, the station serves its audience – and the nation – well.

Every week, around 11 million people tune in to Radio 4, with many of its programmes enjoying a large, dedicated following. In addition, it has built up a huge digital footprint with the largest weekly number of online listeners of any BBC Radio station. Radio 4 Extra is another service valued by many, offering an opportunity to catch up on the best in comedy, drama and entertainment.

With so many appreciating what Radio 4 offers, this book gives you a chance to enjoy the station in another way. There are special sudokus, word searches, anagrams, criss-crosses and coded crosswords, as well as many other puzzles based on the programmes and presenters we know so well. Also included are some rounds of trivia to test your knowledge and some "strange but true" incidents to deliberate over.

I very much hope you enjoy these puzzles and that, like this much-loved station, they will bring you a great deal of pleasure.

Good luck and happy puzzling.

Neil Somerville

# ANAGRAMS

Unscramble the following to discover some well-known programmes.

1. ADMINISTER GREEN QUOTES

2. WALK ON IN DELIGHT

3. GIVES ALERT

4. ADORE TOUCHING BASS

5. ISN'T LESS DISCARDED?

# CRISS-CROSS: RADIO 4

Radio 4 is a celebration of curiosity, knowledge and entertainment, with the following just a sample of areas to listen to and appreciate. Find places for them all in the grid.

**4-letter words**
Arts
Film
Food
News
Quiz
Talk

**5-letter words**
Books
Drama
Media
Money
Music

**6-letter words**
Comedy
Health
Nature
Poetry
Travel

**7-letter words**
Cooking
Culture
History
Science
Stories
Weather
Worship

**8-letter words**
Birdsong
Language
Politics
Religion

**9-letter words**
Gardening
Panel game

**10-letter words**
Discussion
Statistics

# TRIVIA

1. Who came all the way from Great Portland Street to play *Just a Minute*?

2. On 19 September 2019 John Humphrys presented his last edition of the *Today* programme after 32 years on the show. Among the special guests were two former Prime Ministers – David Cameron and Tony Blair – and a comedian. Who was the comedian?

3. *Dead Ringers* have impersonated many BBC broadcasters but which announcer supposedly said, "If satin sheets could talk, they would sound like me"?

4. Which presenter of *Brain of Britain* often said in response to a wrong but entertaining answer, "Ah, would that it were, would that it were"?

5. In *Round the Horne*, who was Julian's friend?

6. Arthur Dent made his first appearance in a series which famously began on Radio 4. What was the series?

7. Which version of the English Dictionary is used in *I'm Sorry I Haven't a Clue*?

8. *Front Row* began in 1998 after major schedule changes were made on Radio 4. What programme did it replace?

9. Who hosts the comedy "Show and Tell" series *Nature Table*?

10. Who, in his programmes, came "to no serious conclusions" and ended with "If you have been, thanks for listening"?

# NAME BUILDER

The letters of a name of a well-known contributor have been numbered one to nine. Solve the clues to discover who it is.

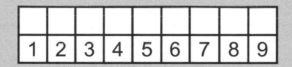

Letters 6, 2, 5 and 4 give us a job to do

Letters 3, 7, 2 and 9 give us something genuine

Letters 5, 6, 3, 8, 2 and 1 give us a brook

Letters 1, 2, 4 and 7 give us something to create

Letters 4, 8, 5, 6, 3, 7 and 9 give us a bird of prey

# MYSTERY SUDOKU

Complete the grid so that every row, column and 3 × 3 box contains the letters ADEHIMOSW in any order. One row or column contains a programme title. What is it?

|   |   | H | W | M |   |   |   |   |
|---|---|---|---|---|---|---|---|---|
| A | W |   |   | O |   | E |   | M |
|   |   |   |   | S |   |   |   |   |
| W |   | M |   |   | I | O |   |   |
|   |   |   |   |   |   |   |   |   |
|   |   | E | M |   |   |   | I | H |
|   |   |   | A |   |   |   |   |   |
| S |   | O |   | I |   |   | H | D |
|   |   |   |   | W | H | M |   |   |

# THE NOW SHOW – PHOBIAS

For many years *The Now Show* has entertained audiences by taking a fun look at news and much else besides. Among the many things considered were some of the world's weirdest phobias. Phobophobia is a fear of phobias but what do the following mean? Take your pick.

1. **Alektorophobia**
   a) Fear of knees
   b) Fear of chickens
   c) Fear of feathers

2. **Koinoniphobia**
   a) Fear of rooms
   b) Fear of pins
   c) Fear of string

3. **Novercaphobia**
   a) Fear of your step-mother
   b) Fear of getting wrinkles
   c) Fear of injections

4. **Siderodromophobia**
   a) Fear of relatives
   b) Fear of anything new
   c) Fear of trains

# ODD ONE OUT

Over many years *Profile* has provided insights into those making the news. Each of the letters of this long-running series are displayed below but which is the odd one out and why?

**8**

# CRYPTOGRAM

Solve the cryptogram to discover an observation Roald Dahl made when appearing on *Desert Island Discs*. To give you a start, O = L and V = R.

| E | N | | E | J | | E | A | I | U | J | J | E | F | O | B, |
|---|---|---|---|---|---|---|---|---|---|---|---|---|---|---|---|
| | | | | | | | | | | | | | | L | , |

| W | K | N | B | V | | O | E | J | N | B | C | E | C | R | | N | U |
|---|---|---|---|---|---|---|---|---|---|---|---|---|---|---|---|---|---|
| | | | | R | | L | | | | | | | | | | | |

| R | V | B | W | N | | A | T | J | E | D, | | N | U | | L | V | E | N | B |
|---|---|---|---|---|---|---|---|---|---|---|---|---|---|---|---|---|---|---|---|
| R | | | | | | | | | | , | | | | | | R | | | |

| W | F | J | U | O | T | N | B | | V | T | F | F | E | J | H |
|---|---|---|---|---|---|---|---|---|---|---|---|---|---|---|---|
| | | | | L | | | | | R | | | | | | |

# WORD SEARCH: TODAY PRESENTERS

All of the following have helped get our days off to a good, well-informed start by presenting the *Today* programme. Seek them out in the word search.

Andrew Marr
Anna Ford
Barry Norman
Brian Redhead
Carolyn Quinn
Edward Stourton
Evan Davis
Jack de Manio
James Naughtie
Jenni Murray

John Humphrys
John Timpson
Justin Webb
Martha Kearney
Nick Robinson
Nigel Rees
Peter Hobday
Robert Robinson
Sarah Montague

```
D B J W M N O J A C K D E M A N I O U
E R Y N O O O N V F U T U Y N S R G N
S I A U K K N S Z M Z J A O A O N I O
I A N K L A U B P X M D S R B L B R T
V N H C F J I K V M B N A E L B J Y R
A R U O G Y K L N O I H R E E B S S U
D E R B E J U I H B M T A W Y K P Z O
N D A M E U G R O O R N N E G L L J T
A H N Y S E E R N O S I N H E N O F S
V E D S L T K T B E T R W B O H O X D
E A R R E C A I J S A Y P Q N J N Y R
M D F P I G N N U E U C L H P M P H A
A E W N U S O J K T L Q U U P I X I W
S R M E O M Y A R R U M I N N E J W D
P A A N D O H V P N P G M E R U R P E
X L R S V T E I T H G U A N S E M A J
K L R R R U C A R O L Y N Q U I N N M
T A M A H E G Y X S E V V N D A V A S
U V M W R S S N A M R O N Y R R A B K
```

# CODED CROSSWORD

Each letter of the alphabet has been replaced by a number. To solve the puzzle, you must decide which letter is represented by which number. To help you start, one of the words has been partly filled in. When you have solved the code, complete the bottom grid to discover what *Farming Today* announced was going on sale as an April Fool.

| 1 | 2 | 3 | 4 | 5 | 6 | 7 | 8 | 9 | 10 | 11 O | 12 | 13 |
|---|---|---|---|---|---|---|---|---|----|----|----|----|
| 14 A | 15 | 16 | 17 | 18 | 19 | 20 | 21 | 22 | 23 | 24 | 25 | 26 T |

| | | | | | | | | | | |
|---|---|---|---|---|---|---|---|---|---|---|
| 17 | 4 | 3 | 14 | 13 | 13 | 16 | | 6 | 4 | 21 | 9 |

# TRUE OR FALSE?

Decide whether the following statements are true or false.

1. The former Prime Minister Harold Wilson chose his pipe as his luxury on *Desert Island Discs*.
2. Mary Whitehouse once presented *Feedback*.
3. In *The Archers*, Tony Blackburn was guest DJ at a party held after the 2019 Ambridge summer fete.
4. Gillian Reynolds was once a presenter on *Today*.
5. While presenting *PM* Valerie Singleton once threw a cup of water over fellow presenter Hugh Sykes.
6. Noel Edmonds presented several editions of *Home Truths*.
7. On New Year's Eve 2002 a mistake occurred which meant listeners did not hear the bongs from St Stephen's tower chiming in the new year.
8. The first time the game now known as Mornington Crescent was played on *I'm Sorry I Haven't a Clue* it was called Goodge Street.

# PROGRAMME BUILDER

The letters of a series (two words) have been numbered one to nine. Solve the clues to discover what it is, as well as something you may also enjoy.

Letters 1, 6 and 5 give us an amount

Letters 9, 2, 8 and 4 give us a spiral

Letters 7, 4, 8 and 5 give us something thin

Letters 1, 6, 5 and 2 give us a type of wrestling

Letters 4, 3, 7, 9, 8, 2, 6 and 1 give us something scrumptious

| | | | | | | | | |
|---|---|---|---|---|---|---|---|---|
| 1 | 2 | 3 | 4 | 5 | 6 | 7 | 8 | 9 |

# MISSING LETTERS

The vowels have been removed from ten programme titles. What are the programmes?

1. MSRRYHVNTCL

2. NRTM

3. THNBLVBLTRTH

4. TWTFTHDY

5. MRRLSS

6. DDRNGRS

7. NTCH

8. LWNCTN

9. NLYSS

10. GDRD

# DESERT ISLAND LUXURY

Match the celebrity to the luxury item you think they chose to take away with them when appearing on *Desert Island Discs*.

1. Paul Merton

a) Cello

2. Archbishop Desmond Tutu

b) Radio

3. John Peel

c) Banjo

4. John Humphrys

d) Ice-cream-making machine

5. Rory Bremner

e) Football

6. Billy Connolly

f) Bed

# ANAGRAMS

Unscramble the following to discover some experts who often appear on *Gardeners' Question Time*.

1. THANKS, IN BEAN WIN

2. FEW BOLD BOWER

3. NOW LATEST WHIM

4. LIKED WINNERS CHAT

5. GOOD. WIN A PEPPER!

# WORD SEARCH:
# THE LIFE SCIENTIFIC

The long-running series *The Life Scientific* has featured interviews with many leading scientists about aspects of their work. Below is a list of some of the items discussed. Find them in the grid.

| | |
|---|---|
| Algae | Fungi |
| Antarctica | Memory |
| Bees | Nutrition |
| Botany | Pluto |
| Brewing | Ribosomes |
| Dark Energy | Saturn |
| Dark Matter | Stegosaurs |
| Flood Control | Sun |
| Fossils | Volcanoes |
| Fracking | |

```
H A S J A Y H S L I S S O F P S W
X N E C Y R M A T X B L W S A E C
E O M E G O D L L Y I G T E D O N
L I O Z J M R C V P T E F A G N F
E T S R V E T Z Z F G R E G N A L
R I O M E M G V U O A U I L I C O
E R B Y Q P Q V S C C E H A W L O
T T I J F K B A K O I P W A E O D
T U R S W R U I Z B T E Y X R V C
A N I Q T R N P W Z C J K T B C O
M T R G S G L N Y J R N Q T Z O N
K Z I U N U V N G B A A Q E V F T
R P M X T U A U B O T A N Y R A R
A B N O F A F E S E N P X T R Q O
D R E N U S S J B R A P G L U T L
Y G L E C D A R K E N E R G Y F P
J L J H S E A N Y I K V G J T A L
```

# MINI SUDOKU: STUDIO

With the studio being the heart of many a Radio 4 production, let it also be the heart of this puzzle. Complete the grid so that every row, column and 2 × 3 box contains the letters that make up the word "Studio".

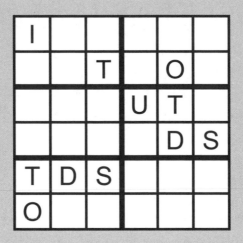

# A PICTURE POSER

What series is suggested by the following?

# CRYPTOGRAM

Over the decades the *Gardeners' Question Time* panel have answered a great many questions including, "What is the ideal gift for a gardener?" To find out what was suggested, solve the cryptogram. To give you a start, D = W and W = M.

| Z | | U | E | E | B | | C | Y | D | | I | Z | V | L | | E | R |
|---|---|---|---|---|---|---|---|---|---|---|---|---|---|---|---|---|---|
| | | | | | | | | | W | | | | | | | | |

| N | Y | H | Z | J | Y | F | L | N | | E | L | | M | Z | W | | R | L | E | W |
|---|---|---|---|---|---|---|---|---|---|---|---|---|---|---|---|---|---|---|---|---|
| | | | | | | | | | | | | | | | M | | | | | M |

| J | A | Y | | U | Z | L | B | Y | C | 'N | | R | L | F | V | J | N |
|---|---|---|---|---|---|---|---|---|---|---|---|---|---|---|---|---|---|
| | | | | | | | | | | ' | | | | | | | |

| Z | C | B | | H | A | V | T | T | V | Y | N |
|---|---|---|---|---|---|---|---|---|---|---|---|
| | | | | | | | | | | | |

# ON TRACK

Starting with the circled letter and moving one letter at a time, either horizontally or vertically, find four gentlemen who have kept track of many a quiz.

| R | U | E | S | V | I | D |
|---|---|---|---|---|---|---|
| S | S | E | D | A | I | M |
| E | L | R | H | C | T | I |
| L | E | G | E | L | I | N |
| L | D | I | P | L | C | C |
| V | A | N | A | G | A | A |
| I | E | S | U | L | M | B |

# CROSSWORD

## Across

**6** Not poetry (5)
**7** Long-running investigative programme (8)
**10** Tricky (7)
**11** Part of a programme (7)
**12** The arts (7)
**13** Spicy stew (7)
**14** Radio presenter (11)
**19** Apt read (anag) (7)
**21** Vehicle for *The Archers*? (7)
**23** Programme for blind and visually impaired (2,5)
**25** More convenient (7)
**26** Dairy cattle breed (8)
**27** Current major programme (5)

## Down

**1** Programme enabling readers to talk to writers (8)
**2** "Seen this before" feeling (4,2)
**3** Humphrey Lyttelton, e.g. (10)
**4** Mentioned in many a traffic report (4)
**5** Picture house (6)
**6** Fish (6)
**8** From the dairy at Bridge Farm (7)
**9** Fidgety (5)
**13** Record player (10)
**15** Doubter (anag) (7)
**16** Restores (8)
**17** Wireless (5)
**18** Bird of prey (6)
**20** Cast of many a drama (6)
**22** XC (6)
**24** Greet (4)

# LETTER DROP

The letters in each of the columns need to be entered into the squares immediately below, but not necessarily in the same order. By placing the letters in the correct places you will discover what Jenny Cuffe said about *File on 4*.

# PRESENTERS

Match the presenter to the programme they present.

1. *Profile*                           a) Jay Rayner

2. *The Elephant in the Room*          b) Amol Rajan

3. *You and Yours*                     c) Carolyn Quinn

4. *The Life Scientific*               d) Evan Davis

5. *The Unbelievable Truth*            e) Michael Rosen

6. *The Kitchen Cabinet*               f) David Mitchell

7. *The Media Show*                    g) Mark Coles

8. *The Bottom Line*                   h) Sarah Millican

9. *The Westminster Hour*              i) Professor Jim Al-Khalili

10. *Poetry Please*                    j) Winifred Robinson

# WORD LADDER

It is possible to listen to Radio 4 in many ways but for some, especially cricket enthusiasts keen to follow the latest tournaments on *Test Match Special*, Radio 4 Long Wave remains an essential service. In this word ladder, change one letter at a time to turn "Long" into "Wave".

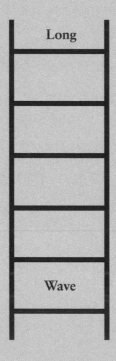

Long

Wave

# CODED CROSSWORD

Each letter of the alphabet has been replaced by a number. To solve the puzzle, you must decide which letter is represented by which number. To help you start, one of the words has been partly filled in. When you have solved the code, complete the bottom grid to discover a popular book that has been adapted for Radio 4. Who wrote it?

| 21 | 18 | 20 | 4 | 7 | 26 | | 20 | 7 | 7 | 10 | 20 | 19 |
|----|----|----|----|----|----|----|----|----|----|----|----|----|
| 2 | | 18 | | 10 | | | 20 | | 23 | | 3 | |
| 8 | 3 | 5 | 18 | 10 | 7 | 21 | | 21 | 7 | 5 | 20 | 26 | 17 | 21 |
| 17 | | 9 | | 7 | | 10 | | 10 | | 18 | | 25 |
| 17 | 10 | 14 | 21 | 5 | 10 | 20 | 16 | 10 | 5 | | 22 | 5 | 10 | 24 |
| | | 20 | | 5 | | 10 | | | 19 | | 1 |
| 2 | 10 | 19 | 19 | 3 | | 19 | 9 | 18 | 24 | 15 | 16 | 26 | 7 |
| 10 | | | | 17 | | 14 | | 3 | | | 22 |
| 4 | 20 | 5 | 6 | 9 | 26 | 21 | 10 | | 18 | 5 | 20 | 12 | 15 |
| 16 | | 9 | | | 26 | | 2 | | 22 |
| 7 | 19 | 10 | 20 | | 11 | 9 | 21 | 22 T | 26 | 17 N | 14 | 10 | 13 | 13 |
| 26 | | 19 | | 20 | | 21 | | 17 | | 3 | | 10 |
| 20 | 25 | 20 | 26 | 17 | 21 | 22 | | 2 | 10 | 20 | 5 | 21 | 20 | 15 |
| 2 | | 8 | | 3 | | | 20 | | 21 | | 18 |
| 22 | 5 | 15 | 26 | 17 | 25 | | 13 | 19 | 3 | 22 | 18 | 2 |

| 1 | 2 | 3 | 4 | 5 | 6 | 7 | 8 | 9 | 10 | 11 | 12 | 13 |
|---|---|---|---|---|---|---|---|----|----|----|----|----|
| | | | | | | | | | | | | |

| 14 | 15 | 16 | 17 N | 18 | 19 | 20 | 21 | 22 T | 23 | 24 | 25 | 26 I |
|----|----|----|----|----|----|----|----|----|----|----|----|----|
| | | | | | | | | | | | | |

| | | | | | | |
|---|---|---|---|---|---|---|
| 7 | 9 | 18 | 24 | 3 | 3 | 17 |

# MYSTERY SUDOKU

Complete the grid so that every row, column and 3 × 3 box contains the letters AEGHILMRT in any order. One row or column contains a seven-letter name of someone who has featured in many a drama. Who is it?

| | H | | | | | | | |
|---|---|---|---|---|---|---|---|---|
| | | T | L | | | | R | | I |
| | R | M | E | | T | | | |
| | | | I | | | E | | |
| E | I | | | M | | | A | L |
| | | A | | | R | | | |
| | | | A | | I | M | G | |
| T | | E | | | H | A | | |
| | | | | | | L | | |

# A PICTURE POSER

What series is suggested by the following?

# ANAGRAMS

Unscramble the following to reveal titles of programmes which are concerned with the outdoors, nature or environment.

1.  O! THE FATTY WEED

2.  IN LARGE REGIONS

3.  RATE BLUE ANT

4.  LAMB GRINS

5.  COPY ONE TURN

# WHAT THEY SAID

The following are quotes but with some of the words missing. What did they actually say?

1. Ian Holm, talking of the 1981 Radio 4 production of *The Lord of the Rings*: "It was made, I suppose, at a time when the BBC took risks and there used to be more opportunity for...
   a) experimentation."
   b) re-interpreting the classics."
   c) unconventional work."

2. Presenter Jane Garvey stated that "*Woman's Hour* is like...
   a) a stately galleon in full sail."
   b) a journey through interesting landscapes."
   c) a box of delights."

3. Former Director-General John Birt said that the qualities of the *Today* programme (and its presenters) are "cheerfulness, which is an important quality in the morning, humour, sharpness and...
   a) tuning into the stories that matter."
   b) political savvy."
   c) staying one step ahead."

# STRANGE BUT TRUE

Why were listeners surprised when listening to *Thought for the Day* on Good Friday in 1980?

a) The talk was being given by the Bishop of Reading from the BBC Reading studio. Within seconds of starting, a fire alarm went off, which meant that the Bishop had to quickly vacate the studio.

b) Instead of a recording of *Thought for the Day*, a trailer for a new series of *Just a Minute* was played.

c) The speaker began "May I wish you a belated Happy Christmas."

d) The speaker started to read from his script but found he had brought along the wrong pages 2 and 3. He told the presenters what had happened and this led to a two-minute discussion between all in the studio. As the speaker concluded, "A Thought for the Day with a difference."

# PROGRAMME JIG

The names of five programmes have been cut up into sections. Join the pieces together to discover what they are.

ERT

VES

IN

TI

DI

SCS

ME

QUE

TOD

GAR

IS

DEN

CH

LA

AY

ON

DES

GRE

AT

ND

LI

STI

ERS

TOU

# CRISS-CROSS: THE BOTTOM LINE

In *The Bottom Line,* Evan Davis has talked with many business people, "giving insight into what matters". Below are some of the things discussed. Find places for them all in the grid.

**4-letter word**
Gold

**5-letter word**
Deals

**6-letter words**
Agents
Design
Travel

**7-letter words**
Big Data
Big Egos
Bitcoin
Pricing

**8-letter words**
Ambition
Failures
Gambling

Plastics
Products
Startups

**9-letter words**
Batteries
Inventors
Shortages

**10-letter words**
Corruption
Flash Sales
Insolvency
Leadership

**11-letter words**
Advertising
Franchising
Sponsorship
Turnarounds

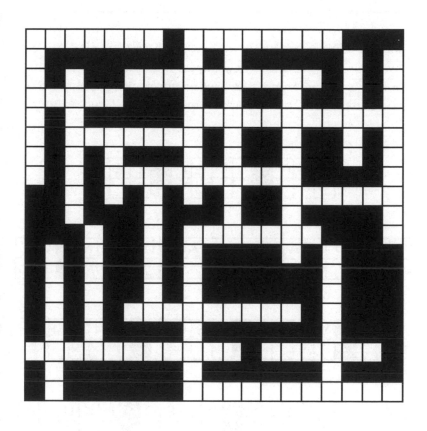

# CRYPTOGRAM

In each edition of *The News Quiz*, much amusement is caused by funny things seen in newspapers and sent in by listeners. Solve the cryptogram to discover an advert which might make you think twice. To give you a start, B = L, U = T and Z = B.

| T F Y | | D E E U | | Z E K |
|---|---|---|---|---|
| | | (T) | | (B) |

SIX FOOT BOA

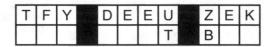

LEPTUAFLUEA. DANN UE

CONSTRICTOR. FREE TO

K VEEQ WEGN. HNAM

A GOOD HOME. VERY

DAFNPQBM, VEEQ NKUNA,

FRIENDLY, GOOD EATER,

BFRNT LWFBQANP

LIKES CHILDREN

# LETTER DROP

The letters in each of the columns need to be entered into the squares immediately below, but not necessarily in the same order. By placing the letters in the correct places you will discover how former Controller of Radio 4, Clare Lawson Dick, saw the role of the station.

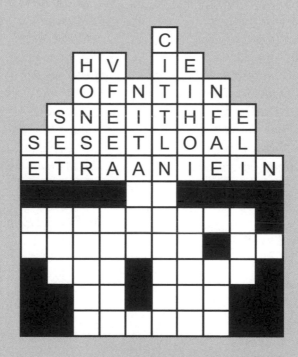

# WORD SEARCH: PROGRAMMES

Radio 4 has a full and varied schedule. Now's your chance to tune in and find the following in the grid.

A Good Read
A Point of View
Analysis
Brain of Britain
Counterpoint
Daily Service
Feedback
Four Thought
Great Lives
Green Originals
In Business
In Our Time
In Touch
Last Word

Loose Ends
Money Box
Moral Maze
More or Less
On Your Farm
Pick of the Week
Profile
Short Works
The Archers
The Media Show
The Reunion
Today
Woman's Hour

```
E C I V R E S Y L I A D P O I B T G I
Z Q T D O U L Y S T R V L C E H Q Z Q
R R J X X G G I K C A B D E E F P E O
M N I A T I R B F O N I A R B I S M N
E T W S D N E E S O O L E F C S R I Y
Y A D O T M A Q E Q R U C K X B E T O
T S F U U O T D L N N P O C N F H R U
N S O W D R L Q A I O F O S Q E C U R
I E U E V A I R O E T R W C M O R O F
O N R I V L V N S H R S I E J J A N A
P I T V F M E M E S Q D D G W Y E I R
R S H F F A S W Q U E I O X I Y H T M
E U O O R Z E V L H A L R O Y N T K H
T B U T N E U E P S T J R U G U A C I
N N G N K R U O H S N A M O W A U L O
U I H I Q D R O W T S A L O E O X Z S
O K T O Y Z W Y E S K R O W T R O H S
C K K P X O B Y E N O M O N Y X O M O
C E O A N R A N A L Y S I S I I T M M
```

# CROSS OUT

Cross out all the letters that appear more than once. The letters that remain, reading from top to bottom and left to right, will spell out something that has often been discussed and praised on *Gardeners' Question Time*. What is it?

| C | I | P | E | N | B | K | G |
|---|---|---|---|---|---|---|---|
| X | F | Z | V | H | T | J | Q |
| A | U | W | B | D | Z | O | Y |
| P | C | V | R | I | G | Y | F |
| N | G | J | H | U | M | X | K |
| T | D | E | S | A | I | Q | B |

# MYSTERY SUDOKU

Complete the grid so that every row, column and 3 × 3 box contains the letters ACEKLMORS in any order. One row or column contains the name of a programme presenter. Who is it?

| | | M | L | R | E | | | O |
|---|---|---|---|---|---|---|---|---|
| O | A | | | S | | | | |
| C | | A | | | E | | | |
| L | | | | | | | | R |
| | | | C | | | A | | M |
| | | | | C | | | L | K |
| S | | | | L | A | O | E | |
| | | | | | | | | |

# A PICTURE POSER

What series is suggested by the following?

# ANAGRAMS

Unscramble the anagrams to discover the names of some Radio 4 newsreaders.

1. HERALDIC GRIDS

2. THAT LUCKY SONG

3. BASE ZONES

4. HASN'T MAIL

5. SUN AREAS

# PROGRAMME BUILDER

The letters of a programme have been numbered one to nine. Solve the clues to discover what it is.

Letters 3, 8, 1 and 6 give us something to exclude

Letters 6, 5, 7 and 8 give us something neat and tidy

Letters 8, 7, 2 and 1 give us a skirt

Letters 5, 3, 4, 6 and 9 give us an itinerary

Letters 8, 9, 2, 6, 3 and 5 give us a trusted guide

| | | | | | | | | |
|---|---|---|---|---|---|---|---|---|
| 1 | 2 | 3 | 4 | 5 | 6 | 7 | 8 | 9 |

# TAKE YOUR PICK

Which of the following are the correct answers about past guests of *Desert Island Discs*?

1. When Elton John appeared, how did the programme end?
   a) Elton hummed along to the theme tune.
   b) He picked out the first couple of bars of the signature tune on the piano before the orchestra took over.
   c) He played his own rendition of the signature tune.

2. Why did the film actor James Stewart cause Roy Plomley problems when appearing?
   a) He called Roy "Ray", despite several polite corrections.
   b) He kept adlibbing and laughing with no real discussion or chat taking place.
   c) He nodded in reply to some of the questions, a response that was not suitable for the sound-only medium of radio.

3. What was unusual about the choice of records made by P. L. Travers, writer and creator of *Mary Poppins*?
   a) All the records she chose were spoken word rather than music.
   b) All the records were backing tracks. While one of her choices was being played, she sang along with it.
   c) All the records were in some way connected with the natural world, including the sound of some animals set to music.

# ON TRACK

Starting with the circled letter and moving one letter at a time, either horizontally or vertically, find four programme titles.

| (E) | D | R | L | E | B | D |
|---|---|---|---|---|---|---|
| O | D | E | I | E | F | N |
| N | R | A | N | S | Y | O |
| S | E | K | I | I | E | B |
| W | E | M | S | D | C | E |
| E | R | O | S | E | N | E |
| O | R | L | E | S | C | I |

# WORD LADDER

*On Your Farm* covers the many challenging aspects of farming life. In this puzzle, take on another tricky task by altering one letter at a time to change the word "Life" to "Farm".

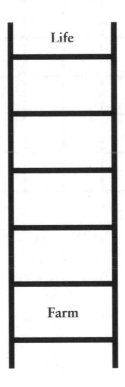

Life

Farm

# ACROSTICS

Solve the clues to discover the name of a presenter in the shaded squares.

| 1 | | | | | |
|---|---|---|---|---|---|
| 2 | | | | | |
| 3 | | | | | |
| 4 | | | | | |
| 5 | | | | | |

1 Head rest
2 Sufficient
3 Polynesian island
4 Anticipate
5 Conundrum

# STRANGE BUT TRUE

In a bulletin read in March 2008, the newsreader Charlotte Green had a fit of giggles and so did many others in the studio. Prince Charles wrote to Charlotte saying the giggling "quite literally made my day." What was the item that caused such amusement?

a) The BBC Sound Archives had just released some of their most unusual recordings, including a parrot reciting Shakespearean dialogue.

b) A species of mountain gorilla which had previously been thought to be extinct had just been found. A recording of this animal was played, which sounded very much as if the gorilla had indigestion.

c) The earliest known recording of a human voice singing.

d) At a comedy festival held in Manchester, top comedians voted on the best one-liner ever created. Charlotte read the joke, but some of the studio team had already heard it and started laughing, which set Charlotte off.

# MINI SUDOKU: SCRIPT

Many programmes depend on a good script and this puzzle allows you to consider this important ingredient in more detail. In this mini sudoku, complete the grid so that every row, column and 2 × 3 box contains the letters that make up the word "Script".

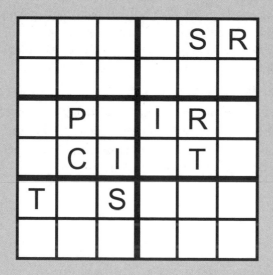

# A PICTURE POSER

This picture suggests one of the items Neil MacGregor selected in the series *A History of the World in 100 Objects*. What is this prized object?

# WORD SEARCH: INSIDE HEALTH

Over the years *Inside Health* has helped clarify and demystify many health topics, including some of the following. Figure out where they are in the word search figure.

| | |
|---|---|
| Alcohol | Obesity |
| Antibiotics | Palm Oil |
| Asthma | Pedometers |
| Flossing | Rickets |
| Gout | Sleep |
| Itching | Touch |
| Measles | Vertigo |
| Migraine | Yoga |
| Moles | |

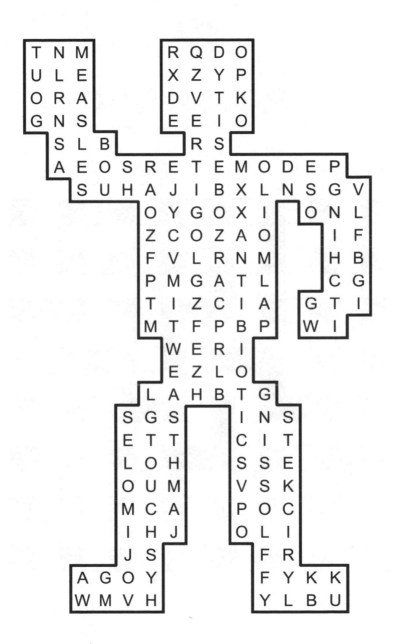

# CROSSWORD

**Across**

8 Scorch (4)

9 Celebrated magazine programme (6,4)

10 Cut back (6)

11 Unit of power (8)

12 Money (8)

14 Broadcast online (6)

16 A point of weekly reflection (4)

17 Disorder (5)

18 24-hour periods (4)

19 Buy in a hurry (4,2)

21 Adrian Mole's Sue (8)

23 Get a programme off the internet (8)

26 Astute (6)

27 Numbers and statistics programme (4,2,4)

28 Atmosphere (4)

**Down**

1 Sue MacGregor hosted this gathering for 16 years (3,7)

2 Programme affords good view? (5,3)

3 European country (6)

4 Out of control (4)

5 Radio 4's detailed examination (8)

6 Brief fall of rain (6)

7 Song for two (4)

13 Fermenting agent (5)

15 Listeners' responses (3,7)

17 Storage place (8)

18 Untidiness (8)

20 Harold ___ dramatist (6)

22 Most enlightened (6)

24 Woodwind instrument (4)

25 Act (4)

# NAME BUILDER

The letters of the name of someone who has caused much amusement on Radio 4 have been numbered one to nine. Solve the clues to discover who it is.

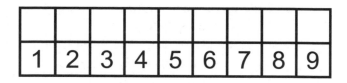

| | | | | | | | | |
|---|---|---|---|---|---|---|---|---|
| 1 | 2 | 3 | 4 | 5 | 6 | 7 | 8 | 9 |

Letters 2, 5, 6 and 4 give us a challenge

Letters 9, 1, 5 and 3 give us something close by

Letters 4, 6, 8, 7 and 1 give us something that will wear away

Letters 8, 2 and 7 give us something unusual

And appropriately letters 4, 9 and 2 give us a conclusion

# LETTER DROP

The letters in each of the columns need to be entered into the squares immediately below, but not necessarily in the same order. By placing the letters in the correct places you will reveal an aspect of *In Our Time* which Melvyn Bragg particularly enjoys.

# WORD SEARCH: THE LIVING WORLD

*The Living World* has featured many intimate encounters and extraordinary observations of wild nature in Britain and beyond. In this word search, take a look at the world opposite and find some of the topics the programme has covered.

Adders
Bittern
Blackbirds
Crayfish
Dippers
Glow Worms
Godwits
Herons
Holly

Jackdaw
Ladybirds
Nightjars
Pine Marten
Polecats
Red Squirrels
Snowdrop
Starfish
Sticklebacks

# ANAGRAMS

In *Just a Minute* it's easy to get tongue-tied and in this puzzle the names of some contestants have become very muddled. Sort the letters out to discover five fine players of the game.

1.  TOP NUMERAL

2.  BY GRAND SHELTER

3.  IS KEEN SPUR

4.  WHY NO TASK?

5.  OH! NICE AS CHALK

# STRANGE BUT TRUE

In 2008 the *PM* programme started a business slot called Upshares, Downshares to chart the economic crisis. What was the unexpected consequence?

a) Listeners sent in theme tunes to introduce the item.

b) The item created so much interest that Steve Punt wrote a spin-off comedy featuring some of the *PM* team, which was broadcast in a late-night comedy slot on Radio 4.

c) The Chancellor of the Exchequer mentioned Upshares, Downshares when making a statement to the House and, following this, the item was frequently referred to by senior politicians and was even cited in parliamentary questions.

# WORD SEARCH: MORNINGTON CRESCENT

Mornington Crescent is a popular yet befuddling game on *I'm Sorry I Haven't a Clue*. In this word search see if you can track down the following London Underground stations, including finding the all-important Mornington Crescent.

| | |
|---|---|
| Amersham | Moorgate |
| Bank | Mornington Crescent |
| Cockfosters | Neasden |
| Colindale | Perivale |
| Dollis Hill | Pimlico |
| Edgware | Ruislip |
| Goodge Street | Stockwell |
| Hainault | Temple |
| Holborn | Upminster |
| Knightsbridge | |

```
S L L I H S I L L O D Z S L D X C V W
K N I G H T S B R I D G E B L L O T O
Q L V P P G H V B O R E R Z O P L N C
V F C D I H Z F F O E V A G L C I E I
N M G V A L N F P Y T N W L S O N C L
T E O M E K S F P X S X G L O C D S M
E L D O X S M I G P N S D E K K A E I
E D P S R I D L U V I H E W N F L R P
R G T D A G K E B R M A L K Y O E C H
T C N H H E A A R I P I C C T S N N D
S G K M W X N T D P U N V O G T D O J
E L I J X C P A E Y H A Y T H E D T S
G M A H S R E M A N L U H S O R L G N
D A S D P L R H U J G L T T L S E N L
O L B A N K I M A L T T E H B B Z I A
O S W Q T B V N T L U M A M O R Y N I
G R Q R J N A C H J P D F R R Z C R Z
F M U D H H L B N L Z Q K P N L G O P
A E V X E S E E E H B C G Y C N V M W
```

# INSIDE INSIDE SCIENCE

*Inside Science* sets out to explore and explain the science that is changing our world. Below are some of the many topics the programme has examined. Put these into the grid and when entered correctly another item the programme has covered will appear in the shaded squares.

Cold Snap
Dark Matter
Drones
Fatty Food
GM Plants
Narwhals
Ozone Hole
Penguins
Solar Farm

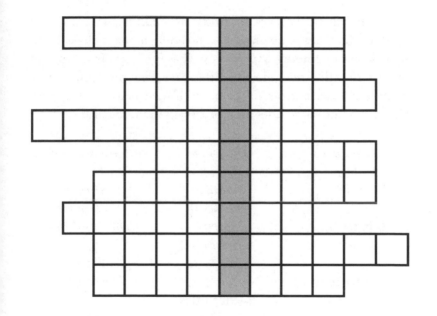

# CRISS-CROSS: BOOK AT BEDTIME

Over the years listeners to *Book at Bedtime* have enjoyed readings of many popular works, including modern classics and new works by leading writers, as well as literature from around the world. All of the following titles have been read, enjoyed by countless listeners from the comfort of their beds. Now is your chance to find these titles and tuck them in on the grid.

**5-letter titles**
Flush
Solar

**6-letter title**
Damage

**7-letter titles**
Capital
Fallout
Hot Milk
The Muse

**8-letter titles**
Addition
Dirt Road

Duty Free
Helpless
Mathilda
The Beach
Trespass
Troubles
True Grit

**9-letter titles**
Dubliners
Lady Susan

**10-letter titles**
Clock Dance
Golden Hill
Persuasion

**11-letter titles**
Dark Corners
First Person
Last Stories
The Third Man

**13-letter title**
Transcription

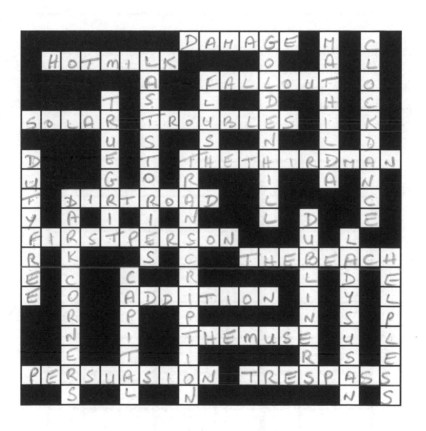

# MYSTERY SUDOKU

Complete the grid so that every row, column and 3 × 3 box contains the letters ABCDEJNOR in any order. One row or column contains the seven-letter name of a contributor to Radio 4. Who is it?

| | | | R | | D | A | E | |
| A | | | | J | | | | |
| | R | J | C | | | | | |
| | | N | | | | | J | |
| D | | R | | N | | B | | A |
| | E | | | | | O | | |
| | | | | | C | J | O | |
| | | | | D | | | | C |
| | D | B | J | | R | | | |

# ANAGRAMS

John Ruskin declared, "There is no such thing as bad weather, only different kinds of good weather." No matter what the weather, the following are all expert at forecasting. Unscramble the anagrams to discover who they are.

1. SLOW PALE SUN

2. AMAZE. SHOCK TRANSFER

3. FRESH AS WICK

4. MY TOTAL ART

5. WELL, HINT SLEET

# TUNING IN

Three programme titles have been entered below. The letters of the titles are in the order in which they appear, reading anti-clockwise. Starting from the S, bottom right, discover which programmes the letters spell out.

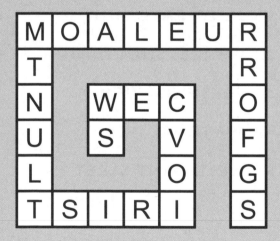

# CODED CROSSWORD

Each letter of the alphabet has been replaced by a number. To solve the puzzle, you must decide which letter is represented by which number. To help you start, one of the words has been partly filled in. When you have solved the code, complete the bottom grid to discover something potentially helpful to Radio 4 listeners.

# PROGRAMME JIG

The names of five programmes have been cut up into sections.
Join the pieces together to see what they are.

THE  LYS  TRU  TOD

FA

SE  ELI     HO

TH    EVA  WOM  UNB

DS      ANS

ANA

IS  AY

BLE      EN

LOO    NG

RMI    UR

# MUSEUM DONATIONS

Over the years many distinguished guests have donated exhibits to *The Museum of Curiosity*. Match the guest to the item they contributed.

1. Sandi Toksvig    a) Privacy

2. Stephen Fry    b) P. G. Wodehouse

3. Jimmy Carr    c) The alphabet

4. Ben Elton    d) Bunch of grapes

5. Henry Blofeld    e) Laughter

# CROSS OUT

Cross out all the letters that appear more than once. The letters that remain, reading from top to bottom and left to right, will spell out a programme. What is it?

| C | L | J | A | O | H | T | M |
|---|---|---|---|---|---|---|---|
| B | K | Y | R | D | G | P | V |
| X | N | H | F | P | M | L | Y |
| D | B | E | O | J | V | W | R |
| A | M | K | S | T | Q | G | U |
| I | X | C | P | F | Y | Z | H |

# WORD LADDER

*Feedback* is Radio 4's forum for comments, queries, criticisms and congratulations. In this word ladder, change one letter at a time to turn "Feed" into "Back".

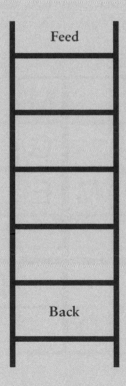

Feed

Back

# MINI SUDOKU: COMEDY

One of the delights of Radio 4 is listening to a good comedy and this puzzle will hopefully also amuse you. In this mini sudoku, complete the grid so that every row, column and 2 × 3 box contains the letters that make up the word "Comedy".

| | Y | | M | | |
|---|---|---|---|---|---|
| | | | C | | |
| | | M | E | | O |
| E | | | | | |
| | | | | D | |
| M | | D | | | |

# A PICTURE POSER

What series is suggested by the following?

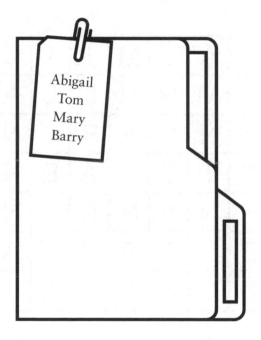

# ON TRACK

Starting with the circled letter and moving one letter at a time, either horizontally or vertically, find five female comedians who have entertained Radio 4 audiences for many years.

| P | A | Y | M | I | I | C |
|---|---|---|---|---|---|---|
| A | M | R | H | L | L | A |
| S | N | E | A | R | J | N |
| K | I | S | S | A | E | N |
| R | N | A | R | E | Y | N |
| E | D | S | B | C | L | A |
| P | E | U | O | J | R | I |

# ANAGRAMS

The following anagrams are all accomplished sleuths who have taken centre stage in many a radio drama. Use your powers of deduction to discover who they are.

1. HE'LL SHOCK MORSE!

2. HI, TRUE COP ROLE

3. AS SHARP RELIC

4. SIMPLE ARMS

5. I'M GREAT

# MYSTERY SUDOKU

Complete the grid so that every row, column and 3 × 3 box contains the letters CHIKLNOTU in any order. One row or column contains the seven-letter name of a programme. What is it?

| | | | C | | N | | | |
|---|---|---|---|---|---|---|---|---|
| O | | | | L | | | | |
| | T | L | I | | | | | |
| K | O | | | | | | | U |
| I | | H | N | | C | L | | K |
| L | | | | | | | H | N |
| | | | | | I | K | O | |
| | | | | U | | | | T |
| | | | H | | T | | | |

# STRANGE BUT TRUE

What was unusual about the luxury item milliner and designer Philip Treacy chose when a guest on *Desert Island Discs*?

a) He said that during the programme he had changed his mind about his choice of luxury item and wondered whether he could have the BBC pencil Kirsty Young had been using during the interview. He said that it would remind him of his appearance on the programme and that he would also enjoy designing clothes with it. Kirsty gifted Philip the pencil.

b) He chose a sewing machine which he had made himself and had actually brought to the studio. Kirsty Young was intrigued by the contraption and Philip demonstrated how it worked. With its gentle rhythmic sound, a recording of Philip's sewing machine was later played on *Broadcasting House* as an item of slow radio.

c) He chose a tailor's thimble. Having taken one with him to the studio, he gave it to Kirsty saying, "It's such an honour to do the show that I wanted to give you something back."

# CRISS-CROSS: JUST A MINUTE

Over the years the contestants on *Just a Minute* have been challenged to speak on a wide range of subjects. Now is the chance to fit some of the subjects into the grid, even though on this occasion it will take more than just a minute.

**4-letter words**
Fads
Hats
Soap
Wine

**5-letter words**
Chips
Jokes
Magic
Power
Rules
Sales
Slang

**6-letter words**
Chance
Poetry

Sharks
Utopia

**7-letter words**
Bowling
Cannons
Customs
Fishing
Marbles
Neptune
Winning

**8-letter words**
Coconuts
Gorillas
Hypnosis
Pinching

**9-letter words**
Porpoises
Puffballs
Surprises

**10-letter word**
Friendship

# MYSTERY TRACK

The name of a series has been entered into the grid. Find the start, then moving one letter at a time, either horizontally or vertically, discover the title.

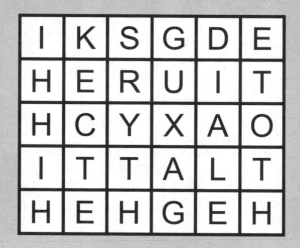

| I | K | S | G | D | E |
|---|---|---|---|---|---|
| H | E | R | U | I | T |
| H | C | Y | X | A | O |
| I | T | T | A | L | T |
| H | E | H | G | E | H |

# MYSTERY WORD

Place a three-letter word in the spaces in each row to complete a seven-letter word. When the grid is completed correctly, a new word in the shaded letters will be formed and is something many a Radio 4 listener finds helpful. What is it?

| A | M |  |  |  | U | R |
| A | V |  |  |  | G | E |
| M | A |  |  |  | R | E |
| P | O |  |  |  | I | C |
| S | H |  |  |  | O | W |
| G | E |  |  |  | I | C |
| N | E |  |  |  | S | T |

# LETTER DROP

The letters in each of the columns need to be entered into the squares immediately below, but not necessarily in the same order. By placing the letters in the correct places you will discover what Jock Gallagher, former head of Midlands network radio, said about Ambridge.

|   |   |   | R |   | L |   |   |   |   |   |   |   |
|---|---|---|---|---|---|---|---|---|---|---|---|---|
|   | O | Y | T | D | A | I | Y |   | H | I |   |   |
|   | D | T | L | S | A | L | L | E | L | I | L |   |
| I | S | E | C | L | I | N | V | U | W | A | K | E |
| W | I | U | L | O | E | T | L | R | W | R | E | C | H |

# ANAGRAMS

Unscramble the following to discover the names of five presenters who keep us informed on current affairs.

1. SO A GREAT HUMAN!

2. THEN MARK A YEAR

3. IQ CAN ONLY RUN

4. BEGUN SURREAL ASK

5. IS ON CHARMS

# TRIVIA

1. "One producer, one randomly generated postcode, and the search for an unheard story." What is the series?

2. Mrs Trellis has frequently written to *I'm Sorry I Haven't a Clue* but where does Mrs Trellis come from?

3. Which comedian presented "Another Case of… " from 2005 to 2011?

4. Which programme aims to "capture the nation in conversation"?

5. What is Ed Reardon's vocation?

6. Who, in 1976, joined the *Today* programme and became the programme's first woman presenter? She also presented *Midweek* for 33 years.

7. Who did Evan Davis take over from when he became the new host of *PM*?

8. Why did the Reverend Geraldine Granger cause so much interest when she delivered *Thought for the Day* on 29 March 2014?

9. In 2001 and 2002 comedian Linda Smith wrote and presented "*A Brief History of…* " what?

10. From where does Alexei Sayle serve up wit, wisdom and illusory baguettes?

# A PICTURE POSER

What series is suggested by the following?

_____

_____

_____

_____

# TAKE YOUR PICK

Which of the following is the correct answer? Take your pick.

1.  When appearing on *Desert Island Discs*, who chose as their luxury a radio tuned into Radio 4?
    a)  Stephen Fry
    b)  Nicholas Parsons
    c)  Sue MacGregor

2.  Sue Townsend's Adrian Mole has enjoyed a long association with Radio 4 and Radio 4 Extra, but when he made his radio debut in 1982 he was not called Adrian. What was he called then?
    a)  Andrew
    b)  Nigel
    c)  Ian

3.  In some of the programmes based on his trawl through the BBC Sound Archives, John Ebdon mentioned Perseus. What or who was Perseus?
    a)  His dog
    b)  His cat
    c)  His "trusty great green tape machine"

# PROGRAMME JIG

The names of five programmes have been cut up into sections. Join the pieces together to see what they are.

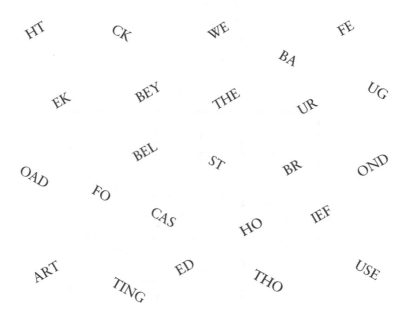

# ACROSTICS

Solve the clues correctly and the shaded squares will reveal the name of a broadcaster. Who is it?

1. Plan
2. Filament
3. Creative person
4. Looking glass
5. Agreement

| 1 | | | | | |
|---|---|---|---|---|---|
| 2 | | | | | |
| 3 | | | | | |
| 4 | | | | | |
| 5 | | | | | |

# MYSTERY SUDOKU

Complete the grid so that every row, column and 3 × 3 box contains the letters EFGILMORV in any order. One row or column contains the eight-letter name of a presenter. Who is it?

| | | L | M | | | | | G |
|---|---|---|---|---|---|---|---|---|
| | I | | | | | | R | |
| | O | M | | | | F | I | |
| | | E | | V | | | | |
| G | | V | | E | | I | | O |
| | | | | G | | L | | |
| | F | I | | | | O | L | |
| | V | | | | | | M | |
| M | | | | | I | R | | |

# CRISS-CROSS: RAMBLINGS

The long-running series *Ramblings* has featured many walks and trails around the country. In this criss-cross, fit in some of the places the programme has visited.

**4-letter names**
Bath
Eyam
York

**5-letter names**
Fowey
Ripon
Truro

**6-letter names**
Bryher
Purton
Ripley

**7-letter names**
Avebury
Bramber

Chilham
Haworth
Mullion

**8-letter names**
Bewerley
Chepstow
Dartmoor
Weymouth

**10-letter names**
Betws-y-Coed
Hathersage
Winchester

**11-letter name**
Aberlady Bay

# DESERT ISLAND LUXURY

Match the celebrity to the luxury item you think they chose to take away with them when appearing on *Desert Island Discs*.

1. Ken Dodd      a) Motorway service station

2. Johnny Vegas      b) The British Museum

3. Noel Edmonds      c) Box of scented soap

4. Ben Elton      d) Hammock

5. Ronnie Corbett      e) An endless bar

6. Dustin Hoffman      f) Kiln

# WORD LADDER

The programme *Bookclub* is almost like a real, interactive book club. Listeners can read a title in advance of the programme and then have the chance to put questions to the author. In this word ladder, changing one letter at a time, turn "Book" into "Club".

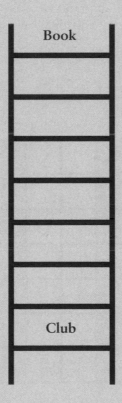

Book

Club

# MYSTERY SERIES

Place the words horizontally into the grid so that in the two shaded columns the name of a well-known series will be revealed. To give you a start, two letters have already been entered.

Éclair
Inuits
Midday
Review
Sketch
Strobe
Throne

| 1 | | | | | |
|---|---|---|---|---|---|
| 2 | | | | | |
| 3 | | | O | | |
| 4 | | | | | |
| 5 | | | | | |
| 6 | | | I | | |
| 7 | | | | | |

# CRYPTOGRAM

While *I'm Sorry I Haven't a Clue* enjoys a great following on Radio 4, solve the cryptogram to reveal a wry observation from the Chairman. To give you a start, N = R, Z = C and G = L.

| F | | X | S | H | F | Z | L | | P | N | S | K | | H | B | L |
|---|---|---|---|---|---|---|---|---|---|---|---|---|---|---|---|---|
| | | | | | | C | | | | R | | | | | | |

| A | B | L | L | N | | V | L | F | Y | B | H | | S | P | | H | B | F | A |
|---|---|---|---|---|---|---|---|---|---|---|---|---|---|---|---|---|---|---|---|
| | | | | R | | | | | | | | | | | | | | | |

| V | L | L | I | 'A | | D | S | A | H | R | T | Y, | | V | L | 'O | L |
|---|---|---|---|----|---|---|---|---|---|---|---|----|---|---|---|----|---|
| | | | | ' | | | | | | | | , | | | | ' | |

| N | L | Z | L | F | O | L | J | | T | | G | F | H | H | G | L |
|---|---|---|---|---|---|---|---|---|---|---|---|---|---|---|---|---|
| | | C | | | | | | | L | | | | | | | L |

| S | O | L | N | | X | S | | G | L | H | H | L | N | A |
|---|---|---|---|---|---|---|---|---|---|---|---|---|---|---|
| | | | R | | | | | L | | | | | R | |

# WORD SEARCH: THE ARCHERS

Since *The Archers* started in 1950, the residents of Ambridge have entertained millions with their trials and tribulations. In this word search seek out the following well-known characters.

Adam
Alan
Alistair
Brian
Clarrie
David
Eddie
Emma
Harrison
Helen
Jennifer

Jill
Jolene
Kate
Lily
Lynda
Neil
Phoebe
Ruairi
Tony
Will

```
Z E A Z Y E I D D E S X U O H
A S D I V A D A W I B A M H C
J I N Q E X D B D F D M A T M
M T W N F Y B H B N D M D R V
L G C X O H M Q N D Y E A O S
E I X J O L E N E R A L A N G
R W L D Z Q Q H J W U I I K H
I C J Y W E T A K S T A J S A
A L N I Y K H L M Z R N I N R
T A A F L E L I P X E Y L R R
S R I L U L L E C L K Y Q D I
I R R R N I I N E T U P Z M S
L I B A Z B W H P H O E B E O
A E E R E F I N N E J K Z H N
Y E G N W H P Z T O N Y H G V
```

# CROSSWORD

## Across

8 Hear again (6)
9 Paul Lewis looks after (5,3)
10 Fit together well (8)
11 Wheel cover (6)
12 Talented (6)
13 Get a programme from off the internet (8)
14 Oversees Mornington Crescent etc. (4,3)
16 Remnants (7)
20 Radio 4 arts programme (5,3)
23 Facial feature (6)
25 Untidy writing (6)
26 Borsetshire village (8)
27 Proclaim (8)
28 Groups of singers (6)

## Down

1 Milk pudding (8)
2 Choose (6)
3 Stand across (8)
4 Collapse inwards (7)
5 Haphazardly (6)
6 Emblematic (8)
7 Musical composition (6)
15 Marsupial (8)
17 Radio 4 comments programme (8)
18 Sets off (8)
19 Pullover (7)
21 Tips given by Garry Richardson (6)
22 Yield (6)
24 Reviser (6)

# PROGRAMME BUILDER

The letters of an award-winning series have been numbered from one to nine. Solve the clues to discover what it is.

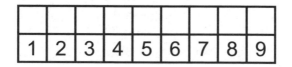

Letters 7, 2 and 5 give us nothing
Letters 3, 8 and 7 give us a marshy area
Letters 3, 4, 5 and 1 give us a moorland hill
Letters 1, 6, 8 and 9 give us untruths
Letters 8, 1, 9 and 4 give us something other

# U-PUN MY WORD

Towards the end of each edition of *My Word*, Frank Muir and Denis Norden entertained listeners with their explanation of well-known phrases. Famously "You can't have your cake and eat it" became "You can't have your kayak and heat it." Below are eight explanations that Frank Muir and Denis Norden created, but what were the original phrases or titles?

1.  My bee eats because I'm a landowner

2.  Throw me the spray to blow foam!

3.  Harp strings hit colonel in the Schumann test

4.  He who Bessie dates is last

5.  I'm cleaning off a white grease mess

6.  Round the weald in a tea daze

7.  Too many kirks spoil Arbroath

8.  Karate begins a tome

# ANAGRAMS

Unscramble the following to discover the names of five presenters.

1. A MAGIC PUBLICAN

2. OR GOT NOBLER!

3. WHAT PRIME STAR

4. RELISH ACCORD

5. MALE ROCKS

# A PICTURE POSER

What series is suggested by the following?

WORK

WORK

WORK ←

WORK ←

# HIDDEN PLACES

For over a decade, Mark Steel has been visiting towns around the UK performing a stand-up show for local audiences based on what he has found out about the area. Some of the places he has visited have been hidden in each of the following sentences. So, for instance, in the sentence "Despite their reservations, they could invent no real reason not to go," the resort of Ventnor is hidden in the words in*vent no r*eal. Mark visited Ventnor in 2019, but where else has he been?

1. You can solve this by logic or by guesswork. Which is it to be?

2. They climbed for days before reaching the summit.

3. A little I think could go a very long way.

4. He took too large a swig and quickly regretted it.

5. He studied art for developing his creative skills.

6. They needed extra gazebos tonight in case it rained.

# A RIDDLE

*My first is in question, not in answer*
*My second is in response, never in reply.*
*My third is in detail, not in fact*
*While my fourth is in exact, never in obscure.*
*My fifth is in clarity, not in unclear*
*While my whole is something now and to hear.*

**What am I?**

# CRISS-CROSS: THE FOOD PROGRAMME

*The Food Programme* sets out to investigate every aspect of the food we eat and over the years has considered all of the following. Now is the chance to sample this culinary collection and fit all these words into the grid. *Bon appétit.*

**4-letter words**
Lard
Pork

**5-letter words**
Bread
Cider
Pasta
Pears
Pizza

**6-letter words**
Cheese
Cloves
Crisps
Garlic

**7-letter words**
Bananas
Mangoes
Oysters
Rhubarb
Vanilla
Vinegar

**8-letter words**
Biscuits
Ice cream
Porridge
Scallops
Soya bean
Tomatoes
Verjuice

**9-letter words**
Chocolate
Marmalade
Mushrooms

**10-letter words**
Scotch eggs
Watercress

**11-letter word**
Bluefin Tuna

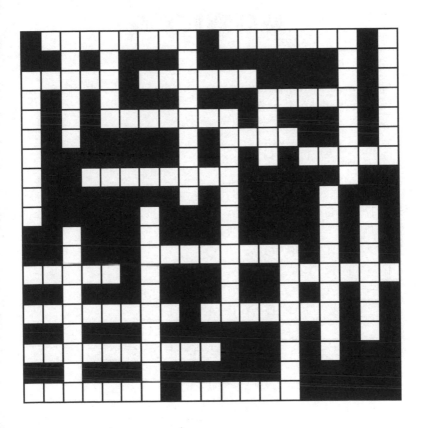

# WORD SEARCH: RADIO 4

Somewhere in the microphone is hidden "Radio 4". Can you track the station down?

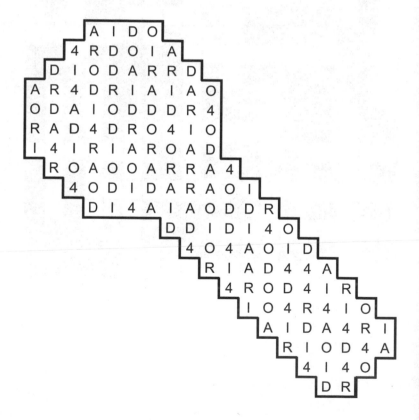

# MINI SUDOKU: ACTING

Radio 4 has won many a prize for drama and exemplary acting. In this mini sudoku, complete the grid so that every row, column and 2 × 3 box contains the letters that make up the word "Acting".

|   |   | T | C | I |   |
|---|---|---|---|---|---|
|   |   |   |   |   | A |
|   | C |   |   | G |   |
|   | N |   |   |   |   |
| G |   | C | T |   |   |
|   |   |   |   |   |   |

# ANAGRAMS

All the following have greatly amused audiences on Radio 4. Unscramble the anagrams to discover who they are.

1. YEAR MAPS

2. I MINE TV

3. MERE TALKS

4. SITING VODKAS!

5. ME AGREE GRAND!

# A TIMELY PUZZLE

Now that we've reached the halfway point of this book, here's a timely puzzle of sorts. Place the following words horizontally into the grid. When entered in the correct order, the letters in the shaded squares spell something familiar. To help, one of the letters is already in place.

Action          Midday
Ballad          Spider
Engine          Stable

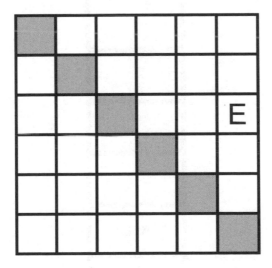

# WORD LADDER

*Ramblings* has taken the listener on many a good walk around the country and now is the time to reflect on the benefit of walking by turning, one letter at a time, the word "Good" into "Walk".

Good

Walk

# CROSS OUT

Cross out all the letters that appear more than once. The letters that remain, reading from top to bottom and left to right, will spell out the name of a book that was adapted into a radio play and broadcast in two parts in 2019. What was the book?

| D | L | J | C | N | F | A | Q |
|---|---|---|---|---|---|---|---|
| T | I | B | W | G | U | O | X |
| V | Z | K | S | H | L | F | M |
| X | U | R | J | A | V | W | T |
| C | H | S | D | Q | P | Z | Y |
| O | G | B | L | I | N | E | K |

# TAKE YOUR PICK

Which of the following is the correct answer?

1. *The Food Programme* has focused on many foods, including a look at "the secret life" of what?
   a) Turnips
   b) Celery
   c) Spaghetti

2. On 1 January 2005, *Woman's Hour* became "*Man's Hour*" for just one episode. Who was the presenter?
   a) Jon Snow
   b) Nicholas Parsons
   c) Melvyn Bragg

3. In 2001, Bob Monkhouse and Suggs appeared in a sitcom called *I Think I've Got a Problem*. It was about a man who woke up one morning to discover...
   a) he could only speak in riddles
   b) he could not stop making puns, no matter what the situation
   c) he could not stop singing at inappropriate moments

# MYSTERY SUDOKU

Complete the grid so that every row, column and 3 × 3 box contains the letters ADGIMNRUY in any order. One row or column contains a name of someone who features in a well-known programme. Who is it?

| | D | I | A | | | | | |
|---|---|---|---|---|---|---|---|---|
| | | | | U | | | | N |
| | R | | | | I | | | |
| R | G | | | D | | M | | |
| N | | | | M | | | | A |
| | | M | | Y | | | G | U |
| | | | M | | | | U | |
| M | | | | R | | | | |
| | | | | | D | R | I | |

# WORD SEARCH: POETRY PLEASE

*Poetry Please* is the world's longest-running radio programme devoted to poetry, celebrating its 40th anniversary in 2019. Over the years it has featured many love poems including those listed below. Seek them out in the heart.

A Marriage
Atlas
Bar Italia
Broadcast
First Meeting
Freight
Hinterhof
Litany
Lovesong
Lullaby

Machines
Muse
One Perfect Rose
Perfect Day
Recuerdo
Skin Full
Tryst
Valentine
Wedding

# CURIOUS TITLES

In *The Curious Cases of Rutherford and Fry*, science sleuths Dr Adam Rutherford and Dr Hannah Fry investigate mysteries sent in by listeners. Some of these mysteries had curious titles but what were the programmes actually about?

1. **The Stressful Scone**
   a) How manufacturers have struggled to find "the perfect scone recipe", including trying to find ways to preserve a scone's freshness.
   b) Whether it is better to put jam on a scone first followed by cream or the other way round, and which method gives the better taste.
   c) How accents start and where they come from.

2. **The Running Joke**
   a) Exploring how fast a human can run and whether we would be faster as quadrupeds.
   b) Why noses tend to run in cold weather.
   c) Why laughter is contagious.

3. **The Phantom Jam**
   a) How musical jamming sessions help creativity and have led to some surprising hits.
   b) What happened to the jam Captain Scott took with him on his ill-fated *Terra Nova* Expedition.
   c) What makes traffic jam.

# PROGRAMME JIG

The names of five programmes have been cut up into sections.
Join the pieces together to discover what they are.

SCI

OP

FE

NKI

OKC

ND

THI

ENT

COU

NTRY

LI

HIP

LUB

SU

IFIC

AY

ALL

OWED

NG

BO

EN

THE

WORS

# CRISS-CROSS: GARDENERS' QUESTION TIME

Over the years *Gardeners' Question Time* has addressed a multitude of gardening issues. In this criss-cross, dig around and plant all the following into the grid.

**4-letter words**
Bark
Soil

**5-letter words**
Birds
Lawns
Pests
Ponds
Trees

**6-letter words**
Apples
Fences
Hedges
Manure
Patios

Plants
Shrubs

**7-letter words**
Alpines
Beetles
Compost
Digging
Trellis

**8-letter words**
Climbers
Cuttings
Diseases
Drainage
Grafting
Layering

**10-letter words**
Containers
Dandelions

**12-letter word**
Caterpillars

# PRESENTERS

Match the presenter to the programme from this roster of best-loved Radio 4 shows.

1. *A Good Read*               a)  Matthew Parris

2. *Round Britain Quiz*        b)  Paul Gambaccini

3. *Broadcasting House*        c)  James Naughtie

4. *Counterpoint*             d)  Claudia Hammond

5. *Bookclub*                 e)  Paddy O'Connell

6. *Any Questions?*           f)  Kathy Clugston

7. *Great Lives*              g)  Tom Sutcliffe

8. *All in the Mind*          h)  Tim Harford

9. *Gardeners' Question Time* i)  Harriett Gilbert

10. *More or Less*            j)  Chris Mason

# A PICTURE POSER

What series is suggested by the following?

# WORD QUEST

In this word quest, make as many words as possible of four or more letters out of the following. All the words must include the letter in the centre, the letter O. No plurals are allowed. One word that can be made has relevance to Radio 4. What is it?

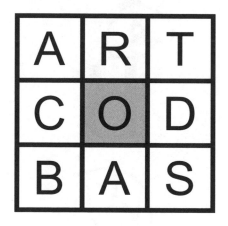

42 words: Excellent
33 words: Very Good

# TAKE YOUR PICK

Which of the following is the correct answer?

1. Which *Today* presenter asked for a minute's silence "while you (Nigel Lawson) compose an apology for daring to suggest you know how I exercise my vote"?
   a) John Humphrys
   b) Edward Stourton
   c) Brian Redhead

2. When considering *In Our Time*, Melvyn Bragg believes "The strength of the programme is…
   a) in its diversity."
   b) in the contributors."
   c) in its ability to surprise and inform."

3. Which iconic pop figure did Matt Lucas nominate on *Great Lives*?
   a) David Bowie
   b) John Lennon
   c) Freddie Mercury

# MYSTERY SUDOKU

Complete the grid so that every row, column and 3 × 3 box contains the letters EFHILMORP in any order. One row or column contains a seven-letter programme title. What is it?

| F | R | H |   |   |   |   |   |   |
|---|---|---|---|---|---|---|---|---|
| P |   |   | E |   |   |   | H |   |
|   | M |   |   | P |   | I |   | O |
| O |   |   |   | H | R |   |   |   |
|   |   |   |   |   |   |   |   |   |
|   |   | M | P |   |   |   |   | L |
| H |   | R |   | I |   |   | P |   |
|   | P |   |   |   | L |   |   | M |
|   |   |   |   |   | F | I | H |

# WHAT THEY SAID

What did the following actually say?

1. Broadcaster John Ebdon said, "I like receiving letters...
   a) that are handwritten... especially with writing I can read."
   b) that make you and I smile."
   c) with stamps on."

2. A listener in a Mass Observation survey in 1993 noted "Radio Four: more like a necessity, but certainly a great pleasure, especially...
   a) the quite unexpected little aural treat."
   b) in hearing so many familiar voices."
   c) its mix between serious and not so serious."

3. Peter Jones speaking on *Just a Minute*: "Is ... in your garden a status symbol? Because there are lots of them in our road!" What was he talking about?
   a) A wheelie bin
   b) A supermarket trolley
   c) A brightly coloured gnome

# CODED CROSSWORD

Each letter of the alphabet has been replaced by a number. To solve the puzzle, you must decide which letter is represented by which number. To help you start, one of the words has been partly filled in. When you have solved the code, complete the bottom grid to discover the definition of "lactic" according to *I'm Sorry I Haven't a Clue*'s dictionary.

# ANAGRAMS

Unscramble the following to reveal the names of five presenters.
Who are they?

1.  **AND BIG CALLER**

2.  **JUMPS PILE**

3.  **IF IN BONNIER WORDS**

4.  **SHONE MIRACLE**

5.  **TRUE LOYAL AIR**

# NAME BUILDER

The letters of the name of someone frequently heard on Radio 4 have been numbered one to nine. Solve the clues to discover who it is.

Letters 9, 3 and 7 give us a dead heat
Letters 4, 8, 1 and 2 give us a country road
Letters 8, 3, 5, 6 and 7 give us a passageway
Letters 9, 2, 8, 5 and 7 give us something that may taunt
Letters 5, 3, 6, 2, 1 and 9 give us something mute

| 1 | 2 | 3 | 4 | 5 | 6 | 7 | 8 | 9 |

# MINI SUDOKU: LISTEN

One of the pleasures of listening to Radio 4 is the variety of programmes the station offers. In this mini sudoku enjoy a chance to "listen" in another way. Complete the grid so that every row, column and 2 × 3 box contains the letters that make up the word "listen".

| | | | | | E |
|---|---|---|---|---|---|
| | N | | S | | |
| | I | | | | |
| | | E | | | T |
| | | | | L | S |
| | | N | | | |

# ONE FROM
# THE OTHER

In each of the following, two programmes have been mixed together. Separate one and find the other.

PAOGETOROYPDLERAEASDE

BSAROTAUDRDCAAYSRTIENVGHIOEUSWE

# CRYPTOGRAM

Solve the cryptogram to reveal an observation by Jenny Abramsky, who served in many senior roles at the BBC, including as Director of BBC Radio. To give you a start, P = W, S = M and T = C.

THE WORLD AT ONE WAS

ACTUALLY THE START

OF MODERN-DAY

BROADCAST CURRENT

AFFAIRS

# WORD SEARCH: WEEKEND PROGRAMMES

There is always a good mix of programmes to enjoy on Radio 4 over the weekend. In this word search seek out and tune in to the following weekend favourites:

*A Point of View*  
*Analysis*  
*Any Questions*  
*Farming Today*  
*Feedback*  
*Four Thought*  
*Last Word*  
*Loose Ends*  
*Money Box*  
*News Briefing*  
*On Your Farm*  

*Open Book*  
*Open Country*  
*Pick of the Week*  
*Profile*  
*Saturday Review*  
*Short Works*  
*Sunday*  
*The Archers*  
*Thinking Allowed*  
*Tweet of the Day*  
*Westminster Hour*

| | | | | | | | | | | | | | | | | | |
|---|---|---|---|---|---|---|---|---|---|---|---|---|---|---|---|---|---|---|
| D | E | W | O | L | L | A | G | N | I | K | N | I | H | T | W | R | R | W |
| V | I | R | H | O | E | J | L | T | X | I | E | F | B | F | I | U | L | D |
| C | M | Q | K | W | M | R | A | F | R | U | O | Y | N | O | O | C | O | W |
| S | R | E | C | S | N | A | Y | N | A | U | C | N | R | H | N | M | S | Y |
| C | K | F | A | P | S | A | T | U | R | D | A | Y | R | E | V | I | E | W |
| Y | D | A | B | B | E | F | Z | T | P | F | S | E | W | D | N | C | U | O |
| A | Z | R | D | E | N | G | H | R | E | I | T | S | B | B | A | V | P | W |
| D | N | M | E | C | N | O | O | F | S | S | B | E | U | P | A | E | X | T |
| E | L | I | E | V | U | F | D | Y | N | R | M | L | O | A | N | I | O | H |
| H | A | N | F | G | I | B | L | I | I | L | B | I | Q | C | Y | L | B | E |
| T | S | G | H | L | A | A | M | E | S | N | N | J | O | B | Q | O | Y | A |
| F | T | T | E | N | N | T | F | O | I | T | O | U | Q | J | U | P | E | R |
| O | W | O | K | A | S | I | N | S | O | J | N | Q | J | G | E | E | N | C |
| T | O | D | C | E | N | S | S | F | A | T | A | X | X | X | S | N | O | H |
| E | R | A | W | G | U | D | V | K | R | O | C | U | O | I | T | B | M | E |
| E | D | Y | F | N | T | I | U | Y | Y | C | B | W | C | G | I | O | Q | R |
| W | F | N | D | E | E | S | D | N | E | E | S | O | O | L | O | O | E | S |
| T | M | A | W | W | S | H | O | R | T | W | O | R | K | S | N | K | Q | A |
| Z | Y | K | E | E | W | E | H | T | F | O | K | C | I | P | S | F | X | F |

# REITH LECTURES

The Reith Lectures started in 1948 with the aim being to advance public understanding about significant issues of contemporary interest. The titles of some of the Reith lectures have been split up. Can you pair the correct titles up?

| | | | |
|---|---|---|---|
| 1. | The Future of | a) | Connect |
| 2. | The Runaway | b) | Identities |
| 3. | Only | c) | Faith |
| 4. | Playing to the | d) | Man |
| 5. | Mistaken | e) | City |
| 6. | Scientific | f) | World |
| 7. | The Persistence of | g) | Horizons |
| 8. | Sustainable | h) | Gallery |

# LETTER DROP

Having just interviewed a contributor on the *Today* programme, John Timpson escorted him to the door. This person suddenly turned round, went back to the table and said something which went out live on air. To discover what was said, which took everyone by surprise, enter the letters in each of the columns into the squares immediately below, but not necessarily in the same order.

|   | E |   |   |   |   |   |
|---|---|---|---|---|---|---|
| M | H | E |   |   |   |   |
| W | X | A | T | D | E | Y |
| Y | E | U | R | E | E | D |
| L | O | C | T | S | I | E |
| E | H | F | U | S | M | I |
|   |   |   |   |   |   | ■ |
|   |   | . | ■ |   |   |   |
|   |   |   | ■ |   |   |   |
|   |   |   |   |   | ■ |   |
|   |   |   |   | ■ |   |   |
| ■ |   |   |   | ? | ■ |   |

# CROSSWORD

## Across

**6** Stabilising material (7)
**7** Radio, TV, newspapers etc. (5)
**9** Assistance (4)
**10** Zeb Soanes e.g. (10)
**11** Ambridge stalwart (2,6)
**13** School period (6)
**15** Unaccompanied (4)
**17** Approximately (5)
**18** Comply (4)
**19** Scattered (6)
**20** Consecrate (8)
**23** Our showman (anag.) (6,4)
**26** Gemstone (4)
**27** Cutter (5)
**28** Dry biscuit (7)

## Down

**1** For general use (3-7)
**2** Artillery piece (6)
**3** Slow-cooked dish (4)
**4** Rain protector (8)
**5** Thought (4)
**6** Loaf (5)
**8** Windflower (7)
**12** Exaggerated stories (5)
**14** Story programme (5,5)
**16** Weather forecasters mention (7)
**17** Container (8)
**21** Standard (6)
**22** Aptitude (5)
**24** Very dry (4)
**25** A single time (4)

# PROGRAMME JIG

The names of five programmes have been cut up into sections. Join the pieces together to discover what they are.

SHO

RT

IA

WOR

KS

OW

BRI

UND

MED

BLI

UL

SH

SIC

QU

SO

IZ

RAM

NGS

RO

TAIN

MU

THE

# ANAGRAMS

Unscramble the following to reveal the names of Radio 4 presenters.

1.  DAD HURT FOREARM

2.  A HUGE MAIN JEST

3.  WARM ERRAND

4.  ON IDEAL HILLS

5.  WILL PAUSE

# ACROSTICS

Solve the clues correctly and something that could be potentially useful to Radio 4 listeners will be revealed in the shaded squares. What is it?

**1.** Proper
**2.** Legal defence
**3.** Aspiration
**4.** Likeness
**5.** Desert haven

| 1 | | | | |
|---|---|---|---|---|
| 2 | | | | |
| 3 | | | | |
| 4 | | | | |
| 5 | | | | |

# TRIVIA

1. What subject does Joshua Rozenberg cover?

2. Which comedian Talks a Little Bit About Life?

3. Who presented *Any Questions?* from 1987–2019?

4. Which programme offered a honey spoon as a prize for solving a cryptic sound clue to a recent news event?

5. In 1998 there was great consternation and many letters of protest when *The Archers* was moved to the 2.00 p.m. slot. What time had it been on before? 12.45 p.m., 1.30 p.m. or 1.45 p.m.?

6. In *Beyond Our Ken*, now heard on Radio 4 Extra, Kenneth Williams played gardening expert Arthur Fallowfield. In response to any gardening question, where did he look for the answer?

7. What is the signature tune of *Desert Island Discs*?

8. What series tracks down the stories behind the scores of well-known pieces of music?

9. Who was the Fat Man on a Bicycle?

10. What is "the antidote to panel games"?

# STRANGE BUT TRUE

What did not go to plan for Evan Davis on the *PM* programme on 16 January 2020?

a) He said that coming up on the programme he would be talking to Robert Shapiro by phone in New York. Little did he realise that Robert Shapiro had just slipped into a seat opposite him in the studio.

b) When he started to interview Robert Shapiro, it transpired he was talking to a different Robert Shapiro than his planned guest. There had been a mix up between two gentlemen who had the same name.

c) When the interview started, Robert Shapiro said that he was told he was going to be interviewed on a totally different subject. In response, Evan Davis agreed to discuss this instead. It led to some amusing repartee and at the end Evan told the audience, "Well that was fun. And I think you'll have to agree, we all learnt a lot from that."

d) Just as Robert Shapiro started to speak, a mobile phone went off. No one knew where the mobile was until, after a few rings, they found it under a console where it had been dropped by a previous contributor.

# MYSTERY FEATURE

The letters of something many listeners appreciate and is sometimes heard on Radio 4 have been numbered one to nine. Solve the clues to discover what it is. The answer consists of two words.

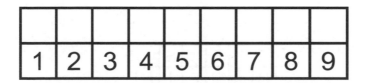

Letters 5, 9 and 4 give us an argument
Letters 7, 9, 3 and 5 give us a portal
Letters 1, 6, 8 and 7 give us something uttered
Letters 4, 8, 2 and 7 give us something untamed
And letters 1, 3, 2, 6 and 5 give us a kind of energy

What is it that many appreciate?

# LETTER DROP

The letters in each of the columns need to be entered into the squares immediately below, but not necessarily in the same order. By placing the letters in the correct places you will discover a description of something regularly heard on Radio 4. What is the description and to what does it refer?

# MYSTERY SUDOKU

Complete the grid so that every row, column and 3 × 3 box contains the letters BDEINOSTU in any order. One row or column contains a word which can be something quite memorable. What is it?

|   |   |   | N | U |   |   |   |   |
|---|---|---|---|---|---|---|---|---|
|   |   | B |   |   | T |   |   | O |
| N |   |   |   |   | B |   | D |   |
|   |   | T | D |   | I |   | O |   |
|   |   | O |   |   |   | E |   |   |
|   | S |   | T |   | O | I |   |   |
|   | N |   | S |   |   |   |   | I |
| B |   |   | E |   |   | D |   |   |
|   |   |   |   | O | N |   |   |   |

# DESERT ISLAND LUXURY

Match the celebrity to the luxury item you think they chose to take away with them when appearing on *Desert Island Discs*.

| | | | |
|---|---|---|---|
| **1.** | Simon Cowell | a) | Acoustic guitar |
| **2.** | Jack Dee | b) | Pillow |
| **3.** | Pam Ayres | c) | Cat |
| **4.** | Princess Grace of Monaco | d) | Cashmere rug |
| **5.** | Mary Berry | e) | Mirror |
| **6.** | HRH Princess Michael of Kent | f) | Large bowl of sugared almonds |

# MYSTERY POEM

The long-running series *Poetry Please* features poems requested by listeners, who would like to hear and share them with others. The poems requested are wide-ranging but all the following are popular poems with a seasonal theme. Fit each of the poems into the grid so that the title of another poem, based on a seasonal image, is created in the shaded squares.

*Digging*                *Soracte*
*Heatwave*               *Thistles*
*October*                *Weathers*
*Postscript*             *Winter*

# CRYPTOGRAM

Decipher the cryptogram to discover the objective of which long-running series? To give you a start, A = L, T = D and S = R.

| Y | J | R | R | E | V | Y | | R | C | | R | Z | J | | Z | J | P | S | R |
|---|---|---|---|---|---|---|---|---|---|---|---|---|---|---|---|---|---|---|---|
|   |   |   |   |   |   |   |   |   |   |   |   |   |   |   |   |   |   | R |   |

| C | M | | K | C | F | V | R | S | H | | A | E | M | J | | D | E | R | Z |
|---|---|---|---|---|---|---|---|---|---|---|---|---|---|---|---|---|---|---|---|
|   |   |   |   |   |   |   |   | R |   |   | L |   |   |   |   |   |   |   |   |

| P | | A | C | C | U | | P | R | | E | V | T | E | B | E | T | F | P | A |
|---|---|---|---|---|---|---|---|---|---|---|---|---|---|---|---|---|---|---|---|
|   |   | L |   |   |   |   |   |   |   |   |   | D |   |   |   | D |   |   | L |

| M | P | S | Q | E | V | Y | | J | V | T | J | P | B | C | F | S | X |
|---|---|---|---|---|---|---|---|---|---|---|---|---|---|---|---|---|---|
|   | R |   |   |   |   |   |   |   |   | D |   |   |   |   |   | R |   |

# QUOTE... UNQUOTE

Since it began in 1976, *Quote... Unquote* has entertained many listeners with amusing and thoughtful quotations. Just as contestants have been challenged about who said what, here's a chance for you to ponder on who made the following statements.

1.  "You've got a goal in life. I've got a goal. Now all we need is a football team."

2.  "What you can do, or dream you can, begin it; boldness has genius, power and magic in it."

3.  "Life is no brief candle to me. It is a sort of splendid torch which I have got a hold of for the moment, and I want to make it burn as brightly as possible before handing it on to future generations."

4.  "What lies behind you and what lies in front of you, pales in comparison to what lies inside of you."

5.  "I love deadlines. I love the whooshing noise they make as they go by."

# ARCHERS TRIVIA

Here's a chance to test your knowledge of the world's longest-running drama serial.

1. What is the name of *The Archers* signature tune?

2. Who or what is Webster?

3. Who carried Lynda from the wreckage after the explosion at Grey Gables?

4. In 2019, which character regaled audiences in Ambridge as well as on Radio 4 with a series of ghost stories?

5. What is the name of the church in Ambridge and the vicar?

6. What was the name of the peacock at The Bull and who accidently ran it over on Boxing Day 2019?

7. Who did Helen stab?

8. Who fell to their death from the roof of Lower Loxley?

9. Early in 2020 The Bull was rebranded and given what new name?

10. Which member of the Royal Family appeared in 2011 to mark the 25th anniversary of the National Osteoporosis Society?

# ANAGRAMS

All the following are anagrams of Radio 4 comedies. Have fun unscrambling these long-running favourites.

1. CAN MUSE OVER HILARITY

2. WENT WHOOSH!

3. VIRTUE BENEATH THE BULL!

4. GRAND DESIRE

5. KEEN AS RE-WORDED

# CODED CROSSWORD

Each letter of the alphabet has been replaced by a number. To solve the puzzle, you must decide which letter is represented by which number. To help you start, one of the words has been partly filled in. When you have solved the code, complete the bottom grid to discover a name often heard on Radio 4. Who is it?

| 1 | 2 | 3 | 4 | 5 | 6 | 7 | 8 | 9 | 10 | 11 | 12 | 13 |
|---|---|---|---|---|---|---|---|---|----|----|----|----|
| 14 | 15 | 16 | 17 | 18 | 19 | 20 | 21 | 22 | 23 I | 24 | 25 | 26 S |

| | | | | | | | | | | |
|---|---|---|---|---|---|---|---|---|---|---|
| 13 | 20 | 10 | 20 | 21 | | 19 | 14 | 16 | 13 | 20 | 14 |

# WHO IS IT?

1. Which weather forecaster has also presented *Gardeners' Question Time*?

2. Which presenter of the *Today* programme is also an expert on beekeeping?

3. Which award-winning crime writer hosted the Radio 4 series *Tales from the Stave* until 2018?

4. Who was a BBC producer, wrote and hosted the panel game *Foul Play*, wrote the successful Radio 4 series *After Henry* (later produced for television) and also created the detective Charles Paris?

5. Who was a BBC producer and created the panel games *Many a Slip* and *Just a Minute*?

# ANAGRAMS

Unscramble the anagrams to discover the names of some newsreaders.

1. SEEN IT ALL

2. OR RECALLS LARCH

3. RECOIL IF RECORD

4. OR CONCEALS IN HILL

5. SEE AND PAID

# MYSTERY SUDOKU

Complete the grid so that every row, column and 3 × 3 box contains the letters ACEHIMRTV in any order. One row or column contains a seven-letter word which is something of value as well as being on Radio 4. What is it?

| | | T | E | | I | H | | R |
|---|---|---|---|---|---|---|---|---|
| | | | | | R | | | V |
| | | E | | | | | I | |
| | | A | I | | H | | | |
| E | | M | | | | T | | H |
| | | | T | | A | I | | |
| | R | | | | | E | | |
| M | | | C | | | | | |
| H | | | I | M | | T | V | | |

# BETWEEN THE LINES

A programme title can be inserted in the blank line so that, reading downwards, seven three-letter words are formed. What is the title hidden between the lines?

| H | E | S | B | R | I | W |
|---|---|---|---|---|---|---|
|   |   |   |   |   |   |   |
| M | D | Y | W | T | Y | Y |

# STRANGE BUT TRUE

How did Nicholas Parsons help Pam Ayres in her first appearance on *Just a Minute*?

a) After making her first successful challenge, Pam found herself with the subject of snorkelling. She said she did not know anything about snorkelling and asked if she could talk about something else. As it was the first time she appeared on the show and Pam had already caused much amusement, Nicholas agreed and Pam ended up talking about the subject "Something else".

b) As her first round began, Pam announced she had written a poem about *Just a Minute* which she recited. It caused such amusement that Nicholas awarded her a bonus point for the poem, even though it had nothing to do with the subject she had been given to talk about. And, as he was feeling generous, he gave her another bonus point so that Pam had the advantage of two points before she had actually started playing the game.

c) He got up and pressed her buzzer.

# A PICTURE POSER

What series is suggested by the following?

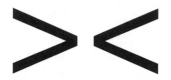

# WORD LADDER

With many now enjoying listening to Radio 4 on their smartphone, here's a chance to enjoy this modern device in another way. Change one letter at a time to turn the word "Smart" into "Phone".

Smart

Phone

# CRISS-CROSS: IN OUR TIME

*In Our Time* has considered a wide range of subjects including those listed below. Fit them all into the grid but, this time, let it be in *your* time.

**4-letter words**
Duty
Nero
Pain

**5-letter words**
Auden
Youth

**6-letter words**
Angels
Coffee
Comets
Dreams
Memory
Merlin
Nature
Prayer
Utopia

**7-letter words**
Dickens
Fairies
Freedom
Planets
Spinoza
Tragedy

**8-letter words**
Feminism
Genetics
Progress
Rhetoric
Stoicism

**9-letter words**
Confucius
Education

**11-letter words**
Imagination
Mathematics

**12-letter word**
Intelligence

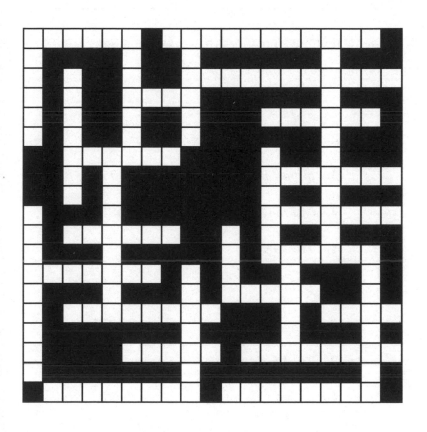

# TIMELINE

Many of Radio 4's favourites have been running a long time.
Match the year to when they started.

1. *Dead Ringers*      a) 1942

2. *Just a Minute*      b) 1946

3. *Money Box*      c) 1950

4. *Saturday Live*      d) 1957

5. *The Archers*      e) 1965

6. *Today*      f) 1967

7. *Woman's Hour*      g) 1977

8. *The World at One*      h) 2000

9. *Desert Island Discs*      i) 2006

# MYSTERY SUDOKU

Complete the grid so that every row, column and 3 × 3 box contains the letters ABGILMNRS in any order. One row or column contains the name of a programme. What is it?

| | | S | A | M | I | | | G |
|---|---|---|---|---|---|---|---|---|
| N | | I | L | | | | M | |
| B | | | | | | | | |
| | | | | | | | | L |
| | | | R | | S | | | |
| G | | | | | | | | |
| | | | | | | | | A |
| | G | | | | N | I | | M |
| A | | | I | B | M | N | | |

# MUSEUM DONATIONS

Over the years many distinguished guests have donated exhibits to *The Museum of Curiosity*. Match the guest to the item you think they contributed.

1. Martha Reeves       a) Boredom

2. Lee Mack            b) Epping Forest

3. Sarah Millican      c) Tempting fate

4. Tim Minchin         d) Pictures of animals in clothes

5. Alan Davies         e) Silence

# TRIVIA

1. Which programme ran from March 1946–February 2004, holding the record as the longest-running speech programme in radio history?

2. In which programme does David Aaronovitch and a panel of experts take an in-depth look at major issues in the news?

3. What comedy series, now available on Radio 4 Extra, was originally called *Crazy People* before changing its name?

4. In 2011 *The News Quiz* featured a special pantomime in which something on Radio 4 went missing. What was it?

5. Who was affectionately known as CMJ?

6. Which sleuth has Bill Nighy played for many years on Radio 4?

7. In an adaptation of *Oliver Twist* broadcast in 2020, from which African country did Oli come from?

8. Who was the voice of The Book in the original series of *The Hitchhiker's Guide to the Galaxy*?

9. In 2001 *Farming Today* and *You and Yours* created a "bit of broadcasting history" by teaming up together. What crisis were these two progammes covering?

10. Who on Radio 4 is depicted as a "consummate fare-dodger and master of the abusive email trying to survive in a world where the media seems to be run by idiots and charlatans"?

# THE TODAY CHALLENGE

In the late 1970s *Today* featured an item about cryptic crosswords. Following this the presenters came up with their own cryptic clue which they challenged listeners to solve. The clue was:

# GEG

The answer is 9, 3. Any ideas?

# TUNING IN

Three programme titles have been entered below. The letters of the titles are in the order in which they appear, reading anti-clockwise. Starting from the O, bottom right, discover what they are.

| O | A | U | C | N | Y | E |
|---|---|---|---|---|---|---|
| N | | | | | | N |
| N | | S | R | Y | | S |
| U | | Y | | R | | P |
| S | | | | E | | A |
| D | N | W | A | T | | O |

# WORD SEARCH: SHIPPING FORECAST

*The Shipping Forecast*, with its place names and familiar phrases, has an almost lyrical quality. As Charlotte Green once observed, it "is the nearest I ever came to reading poetry on air." Mull over the names used in the forecast and find them in the grid.

| | |
|---|---|
| Bailey | Lundy |
| Biscay | Malin |
| Cromarty | North Utsire |
| Dogger | Plymouth |
| Dover | Portland |
| Faeroes | Rockall |
| Fair Isle | Shannon |
| Fastnet | Sole |
| Fisher | South Utsire |
| FitzRoy | Southeast Iceland |
| Forth | Thames |
| Forties | Trafalgar |
| German Bight | Tyne |
| Hebrides | Viking |
| Humber | Wight |
| Irish Sea | |

```
G L P Y A G E R M A N B I G H T N W S
H T U O M Y L P Y S L W C W E A L V G
Y D N U L T F S E X T E N T S A F O K
H J U K N A V O B J N K P V S R B F M
L E E X W O R E I X E A U H O E O P Z
B D B A A E N X S G T I E C U R N F W
O O H R A Q C N C F U R K S T H M I W
R V Y F I V O X A E O A A I H S K S F
E E U L S D I K Y H L R E F E S U H H
G R F E O E E O M L S S T W A S I E X
G T I M L Y R S P P K L I H S L X R S
O Y H S E Z Z T H G I W Y R T G G O I
D E A A T H S O U T H U T S I R E A H
L L M I M U U X D X I M R N C A T G R
O I F K Z E H M N R Y A A L E C F N S
C A E N Y T S T B X X L M D L A B I U
A B C M O A H M R E N I O A A K M K M
E P O R T L A N D O R N R S N E X I L
Y A K B L O R M L S N D C S D Z F V J
```

# MINI SUDOKU: GRUNDY

With their humour, enterprise and many attempts to better themselves, the Grundys have contributed much to *The Archers* and life in Ambridge. In this mini sudoku, complete the grid so that every row, column and 2 × 3 box contains the letters that make up the name "Grundy".

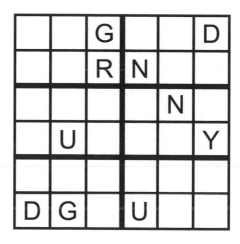

# TOP FIVE

In a 2019 *Radio Times* poll, a panel of industry experts voted on the best radio programmes of all time. The following are the top five programmes listed in alphabetical order. Put them in the order they finished in the poll, from the winner to the programme that finished in fifth position.

*DESERT ISLAND DISCS*

*HANCOCK'S HALF HOUR*

*IN THE PSYCHIATRIST'S CHAIR*

*ROUND THE HORNE*

*THE ARCHERS*

# ANAGRAMS

In the words of Ken Dodd, all the following know how to tickle the chuckle muscles. Unscramble the anagrams to discover who they are.

1. SCREAM BOGUS TRICK

2. HUSH ENDING

3. LOTS JOIN MEN

4. SENT UP VET

5. CARRY BERRY

# CROSS OUT

Cross out all the letters that appear more than once. The letters that remain, reading from top to bottom and left to right, will spell out a character who has often appeared on Radio 4. Who is it and where is this person from?

| F | B | S | N | A | V | H | C |
|---|---|---|---|---|---|---|---|
| W | Y | K | G | Z | J | X | Q |
| I | R | D | H | C | U | F | T |
| X | C | M | Y | W | G | S | P |
| T | K | F | O | N | V | B | J |
| Z | L | Q | I | E | A | D | H |

# CRISS-CROSS: TWEET OF THE DAY

*Tweet of the Day* has featured the songs of many different birds. In this criss-cross, *tweet* yourself to the challenge of fitting all the following into the grid. A pleasant rather than *fowl* task!

**4-letter birds**
Coot
Crow
Lark
Swan
Wren

**5-letter birds**
Heron
Raven
Robin
Snipe
Swift

**6-letter birds**
Curlew
Dipper
Gannet
Linnet
Magpie
Pigeon

**7-letter birds**
Dunnock
Moorhen
Peacock
Red Kite
Sparrow

**8-letter birds**
Starling
Tawny Owl
Woodcock

**9-letter birds**
Blackbird
Corncrake
Goldfinch
Red Grouse

**10-letter birds**
Kingfisher
Woodpecker

# TAKE YOUR PICK

1. What donation did J. K. Rowling make to *The Museum of Curiosity*?
   a) A wand
   b) A dream catcher
   c) Inspiration

2. In an edition of *Word of Mouth* broadcast in July 2019, the most powerful word in the English language was considered. What was the word?
   a) Love
   b) The
   c) Yes

3. Which presenter on the *Today* programme often spoke about the health of his camellias?
   a) Peter Hobday
   b) Hugh Sykes
   c) John Timpson

# A PICTURE POSER

What series is suggested by the following?

A
U
S
T
R
O
P
E
E
U
A
L
I
A

# HEARD AT AMBRIDGE?

*The Archers*, which started as "An everyday story of country folk", is based in the Midlands. The following are all country words which come from the region, but do you know the correct meanings?

1. **Nasle**
   a) Iron rod used by thatchers
   b) The harness of a horse
   c) The smallest pig in a litter

2. **Huff cap**
   a) Fungus
   b) Type of pear
   c) To be in a bad mood

3. **Glouton**
   a) Frog or toad
   b) Dried-up pond
   c) Fallow ground

4. **Spindle**
   a) Handgrips of a scythe
   b) The back end of a cart
   c) A swarm of bees

# CODED CROSSWORD

Each letter of the alphabet has been replaced by a number. To solve the puzzle, you must decide which letter is represented by which number. To help you start, one of the words has been partly filled in. When you have solved the code, complete the bottom grid to discover something often heard on Radio 4.

| 25 |    | 10 |    | 10 |    | 18 |    | 22 |    | 26 |    | 2  |    | 2  |
| 26 | 14 | 25 | 26 | 18 | 12 | 16 |    | 18 | 17 | 14 | 15 | 7  | 26 | 10 |
| 16 |    | 26 |    | 18 |    | 23 |    | 20 |    | 23 |    | 10 |    | 21 |
| 7  | 8  | 15 | 10 | 12 | 19 | 16 |    | 18 | 1  | 16 | 8  | 16 | 2  | 12 |
| 16 |    | 8  |    |    |    | 17 |    | 8  |    | 3  |    | 14 |    | 8(R) |
| 22 | 21 | 16 | 2  | 9  | 11 | 2  | 22 | 4  |    | 16 | 5  | 12 | 8  | 2(A) |
|    |    |    |    | 8  |    |    |    | 16 |    | 2  |    | 16 |    | 13(Y) |
| 16 | 5  | 9  | 19 | 18 | 23 | 16 |    | 8  | 18 | 12 | 12 | 16 | 8  | 10 |
| 26 |    | 2  |    | 24 |    | 17 |    |    |    | 16 |    |    |    |    |
| 8  | 18 | 1  | 16 | 8  |    | 7  | 8  | 18 | 2  | 23 | 22 | 2  | 10 | 12 |
| 13 |    | 15 |    | 2  |    | 19 |    | 5  |    |    |    | 22 |    | 15 |
| 23 | 15 | 19 | 16 | 17 | 17 | 2  |    | 13 | 18 | 24 | 21 | 26 | 8  | 12 |
| 15 |    | 15 |    | 17 |    | 6  |    | 24 |    | 2  |    | 17 |    | 19 |
| 22 | 19 | 18 | 10 | 16 | 12 | 18 |    | 16 | 5  | 12 | 8  | 16 | 17 | 16 |
| 16 |    | 14 |    | 10 |    | 14 |    | 14 |    | 16 |    | 14 |    | 23 |

| 1  | 2(A) | 3  | 4  | 5  | 6  | 7  | 8(R) | 9  | 10 | 11 | 12 | 13(Y) |
| 14 | 15   | 16 | 17 | 18 | 19 | 20 | 21   | 22 | 23 | 24 | 25 | 26   |

| | | | | | | |
|12|21|16| |9|15|9|10|

# MYSTERY SUDOKU

Complete the grid so that every row, column and 3 × 3 box contains the letters ABCEHINRT in any order. One row or column contains a seven-letter name and someone often heard on Radio 4. Who is it?

| T | H |   | B | N |   |   |   |   |
| E | R |   | C |   |   |   |   | H |
|   |   | C |   |   |   | B |   |   |
|   |   | E |   |   | T | C |   |   |
| R | A |   |   |   |   |   | B | I |
|   |   | T | H |   |   | R |   |   |
|   |   | N |   |   |   | H |   |   |
| C |   |   |   |   | E |   | R | B |
|   |   |   |   | A | B |   | N | C |

# A PUZZLING POSER

Someone was listening to a Radio 4 drama. To their annoyance the drama stopped for a short while before coming back on. This person had not touched or moved away from the radio and there was nothing wrong with it. There was also no problem with Radio 4 or the programme transmission. Others had heard the drama in full. What had happened?

# THE MORAL MAZE

*The Moral Maze* has deliberated over many difficult issues. Here is a chance to work out a moral maze with a difference by finding a way from "Moral" to "Maze".

Moral

Maze

# X

Insert the following words horizontally into the grid. When entered correctly the letters in the shaded squares will spell a long-running series in an "x" pattern, a programme which could be beneficial. To give you a start, two letters have already been entered. What is the series?

Answer
Belief
Handle
Impish
Mosaic
Steady

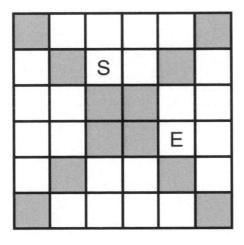

# ANAGRAMS

Unscramble the following to discover the names of some long-running programmes.

1. **HERE CHARTS**

2. **MET THREE IN LINE**

3. **OH TOUGH TURF!**

4. **THE NEAT CHICKEN BIT**

5. **FROM WOOD HUT**

# PROGRAMME BUILDER

The letters of a progamme title have been numbered one to nine. Solve the clues to discover what it is.

Letters 3, 5 and 7 give us a poem
Letters 8, 9, 1, 2 and 7 give us a saying
Letters 4, 6 and 7 give us a mineral
Letters 1, 9, 3, 6, 7 and 5 give us something loved deeply
Letters 7, 2 and 4 give us self-importance

| | | | | | | | | |
|---|---|---|---|---|---|---|---|---|
| 1 | 2 | 3 | 4 | 5 | 6 | 7 | 8 | 9 |

# WORD SEARCH: SOUL MUSIC

*Soul Music* is a long-running series about pieces of music with a powerful emotional impact. All these pieces have been featured in the series and finding them all could well leave you feeling upbeat.

Abide With Me
Amazing Grace
Baker Street
Clair de Lune
Crazy
Fever
Finlandia
Hallelujah
In the Mood
Lili Marlene
Mack the Knife
Nimrod
Over the Rainbow
Redemption Song
River

So What
Somewhere
Stand By Me
Streets of London
Summertime
Swan Lake
Tainted Love
The Boxer
The Last Post
The Skye Boat Song
Waterloo Sunset
We Are Family
Witchita Lineman
Zadok

```
C O Z A D O K H A J U L E L L A H F W
A M L A M A Z I N G G R A C E F W I U
G N O S T A O B E Y K S E H T S A N H
S T R E E T S O F L O N D O N O T L N
L A S T A N D B Y M E T V X M M E A A
P I E O Y V I E P B S E E R A E R N M
V N L L F Z P F Y O R G N E C W L D E
E T D I G E O H P T C S U B K H O I N
S E Z L M L V T H Z D U L Y T E O A I
W D N D V A S E C A O M E L H R S D L
A L H A Y A R T R T R M D I E E U O A
N O A F L A H L Q T R E R M K F N O T
L V S E I E C Z E I A R I A N O S M I
A E H N B R S C V N N T A F I S E E H
K T B O A C H E I V E I L E F O T H C
E O X Z U Z R V L O I M C R E W W T T
W E Y A T E E R T S R E K A B H T N I
R G N O S N O I T P M E D E R A H I W
P D O R M I N F A B I D E W I T H M E
```

# WORD LADDER

During the day Radio 4 keeps listeners informed about national and global news. In this word ladder enjoy the chance to take on the role of turning "News" into "Item".

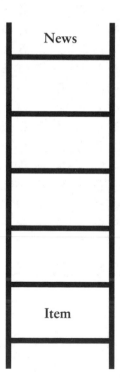

News

Item

# RIDDLE

*My first is in radio, not television*
*My second is in programme, never in series.*
*My third is in episode, not instalment*
*My fourth is in hear but not watch.*
*My fifth is in audio, not in sound*
*And my sixth is in listener, not viewer.*
*While my whole is regularly on Four*
*and both attracts and gets more.*

**What am I?**

# STRANGE BUT TRUE

On one occasion when *Any Questions?* was being broadcast from a village in Devon something unexpected happened. What was it?

a) Jonathan Dimbleby and the panel met up for a meal in a pub before the broadcast. As Jonathan needed to go ahead to sort out the questions, he set off to the venue before the panel. However, on his way, he found himself following a slow-moving tractor and was then further delayed as sheep crossed the lane. The panel took another route and got to the venue in ample time with Jonathan arriving just minutes before the broadcast. Luckily all the questions had been sorted and were ready.

b) One of the panellists, David Owen, knew Devon and agreed to take the others to the venue after Jonathan Dimbleby had gone ahead to prepare for the show. Unfortunately, he ended up in a village with a similar name to the one hosting the show and which was also in the opposite direction. Luckily they made it to the correct venue just in time.

c) The vehicle taking Jonathan Dimbleby and the panel broke down in a lane miles from nowhere. A farmer came to their rescue and took them all to the venue sitting on the back of a trailer. They made the broadcast with just minutes to spare. As Jonathan said, "It was all very touch and go."

# A PICTURE POSER

What series is suggested by the following?

# MIALLND

# WORD SEARCH: WOMAN'S HOUR

In its long broadcasting history, *Woman's Hour* has featured interviews with many leading women, including the following. Find these distinguished ladies in the grid.

Cilla Black
Delia Smith
Edith Evans
Enid Blyton
Helen Mirren
Jane Fonda
J. K. Rowling
Joan Baez
Joan Collins
Joyce Grenfell
Judi Dench
Julie Andrews
Kate Winslet

Linda McCartney
Margaret Thatcher
Mary Berry
Mary Peters
Mary Quant
Maya Angelou
Sharon Osbourne
Theresa May
Tracey Emin
Twiggy
Vera Lynn
Winnie Mandela
Yoko Ono

```
X S L R E O J O Y C E G R E N F E L L
Y N O E F T N Y S N A V E H T I D E S
K I J H S A J O G H D H C C H T X A L
Q L W C R S U J O G I I T N L R I L K
N L F T E H L M L K I V L E I N A E Z
E O W A T A I N T R O W J D N O B D J
R C T H E R E S A M A Y T I D T J N A
R N C T P O A A Z N C C M D A Y O A N
I A I T Y N N C Z W N O D U M L A M E
M O L E R O D P E X R Y A J C B N E F
N J L R A S R K V Y W R L M C D B I O
E K A A M B E R N N E P J A A I A N N
L I B G Q O W U X H C M B G R N E N D
E D L R V U S E R H K K I I T E Z I A
H O A A Y R R E B Y R A M N N Y V W E
V D C M E N S M A Y A A N G E L O U G
H N K A T E W I N S L E T O Y X D E G
H T I M S A I L E D J K R O W L I N G
I E N N T N A U Q Y R A M U Q Y R A M
```

# WHAT THEY SAID

The following are some amusing quotes from Henry Blofeld, Phil Tufnell and Geoffrey Boycott on *Test Match Special* but what did they actually say? Fill the gaps.

1. "I can see a ... walking across the pitch, and what's more it appears to have a limp."
   a) butterfly
   b) seagull
   c) squirrel

2. When Matt Prior had been comprehensively bowled by Australia's Mitchell Johnson, Phil Tufnell said he'd been "feng shui'd". When asked what he meant Phil replied...
   a) "There's now one less on the pitch."
   b) "He's had his furniture rearranged."
   c) "He'd created too much space between himself and the wicket."

3. A Geoff Boycott comment: "Could have hit the ball with a stick of...
   a) celery."
   b) rhubarb."
   c) candy."

# TRIVIA

1. According to the sitcom, what two items are sold along with bags?

2. Who presented *Desert Island Discs* for two years after the death of Roy Plomley?

3. According to Claudia Hammond, D is for what?

4. Fred Loads was a regular panellist on which programme?

5. On Boxing Day 2000 Radio 4 broadcast an eight-hour reading of *Harry Potter and the Philosopher's Stone*. Who was the reader?

6. Who presented *In the Psychiatrist's Chair*?

7. Which fictional detective, created by Francis Durbridge, made his first radio appearance in 1938 and has since featured in more than 30 radio dramas?

8. Which Radio 4 presenter was once in the band The Communards and is now a Church of England priest?

9. Which programme brings two people together to talk about their creative work? The agenda is theirs, there is no presenter and the conversation is free-flowing.

10. In which programme do Brian Cox and Robin Ince cast a witty, irreverent look at the world through scientists' eyes?

# CRISS-CROSS: THE DIGITAL HUMAN

Since it began in 2011, the series *The Digital Human* has explored many different aspects of the digital world including all of the following. Find places for these topics in the grid.

**3-letter word**
Joy

**4-letter words**
Echo
Mind

**5-letter words**
Anger
Bliss
Cameo
Magic

**6-letter words**
Chance
Ethics

Jigsaw
Oracle
Rescue
Vortex
Wisdom

**7-letter words**
Average
Between
Control
Imagine
Secrets

**8-letter words**
Altruism
Detached

Devotion
Friction
Illusion

**10-letter words**
Conviction
Protection

**11-letter word**
Perspective

**12-letter words**
Authenticity
Subconscious

# ON TRACK

Starting with the circled letter and moving one letter at a time, either horizontally or vertically, find four presenters on Radio 4.

| S | H | I | M | U | A | Y |
|---|---|---|---|---|---|---|
| I | E | N | N | R | R | W |
| L | L | O | E | R | F | I |
| A | L | N | J | E | I | N |
| D | I | J | B | D | O | N |
| T | S | U | B | R | S | N |
| I | N | W | E | O | B | I |

# LETTER DROP

The letters in each of the columns need to be entered into the squares immediately below, but not necessarily in the same order. By placing the letters in the correct places you will discover one of the more unusual topics covered by *The Kitchen Cabinet*.

|   |   | A | O | I |   |   |   |   |
|---|---|---|---|---|---|---|---|---|
|   | W | T | H | V | E | S |   |   |
|   | H | E | L | R | P | E |   |   |
| P | I | M | A | O | P | R | D | E |
| H | I | C | H | A | P | R | L | N | S |
| V | O | N | E | N | U | E | A | E | S |

# CRYPTOGRAM

*I'm Sorry, I'll Read That Again* was a fast-paced show of sketches and songs featuring the talents of John Cleese, Bill Oddie, Tim Brooke-Taylor, Graeme Garden, David Hatch and Jo Kendall. It can now be enjoyed on Radio 4 Extra but, in a show originally broadcast in 1966, the Director of Entertainment was asked what sort of audience he was aiming at. Solve the cryptogram to discover his response. To give you a start, G = Y and M = G.

| N | E | G | S | E | T |   | U | J | S | 'B |   | R | S | S |   | B | Z | S | U |
|---|---|---|---|---|---|---|---|---|---|----|---|---|---|---|---|---|---|---|---|
|   |   | Y |   |   |   |   |   |   |   | '  |   |   |   |   |   |   |   |   |   |

| R | S |   | M | T | R |   | S | F | R |   | S | Y |   | R | J | T |
|---|---|---|---|---|---|---|---|---|---|---|---|---|---|---|---|---|
|   |   |   | G |   |   |   |   |   |   |   |   |   |   |   |   |   |

| U | N | G, |   | P | N | B | D | W | N | Z | Z | G |
|---|---|----|---|---|---|---|---|---|---|---|---|---|
|   |   | Y, |   |   |   |   |   |   |   |   |   | Y |

# ROUND BRITAIN QUIZ

*Round Britain Quiz* was first broadcast in 1947 and is the oldest quiz programme still being broadcast on British radio. In tribute to this popular series, here's a chance to try a quiz that will test your knowledge of Britain. Good luck.

1. What is known as "The Granite City"?
2. Which is the longest river in Britain?
3. In which county is the National Memorial Arboretum?
4. On London Underground maps, what line is coloured brown?
5. What is the top pub name in Britain?
6. In which part of Britain would you find Freshwater you cannot drink, Needles you cannot thread and Newport you cannot bottle?
7. Which Welsh town has become known as "the town of books" and is the site of an annual festival?
8. What is the capital of the Isle of Man?
9. Who wrote a seven-volume Pictorial Guide to the Lakeland Fells?
10. What city was once known as Jorvik?

# CODED CROSSWORD

Each letter of the alphabet has been replaced by a number. To solve the puzzle, you must decide which letter is represented by which number. To help you start, one of the words has been partly filled in. When you have solved the code, complete the bottom grid to discover something you can listen to as well as own.

| 16 | | 22 | | 26 | | 19 | | 26 | | 1 | | 15 | | 26 |
|----|----|----|----|----|----|----|----|----|----|----|----|----|----|----|
| 19 | 21 | 4 | 19 | 3 | 6 | 7 | | 4 | 8 | 19 | 11 | 6 | 4 | 22 |
| 18 | | 5 | | 6 | | 7 | | 8 | | 7 | | 16 | | 19 |
| 4 | 13 | 26 | 4 | 8 | 16 | 5 | | 15 | 6 | 12 | 6 | 11 | 16 | 26 |
| 22 | | 14 | | | | 24 | | 5 | | 12 | | 5 | | 25 |
| 13 | 8 | 6 | 15 | 19(A) | 3(T) | 5 | 14 | 17 | | 11 | 10 | 3 | 7 | 25 |
| | | | | 14 | | | | 10 | | 6 | | 3 | | 6 |
| 20 | 19 | 4 | 9 | 13 | 19 | 26 | | 8 | 5 | 20 | 14 | 5 | 7 | 3 |
| 5 | | 11 | | 25 | | 4 | | | | 5 | | | | |
| 5 | 9 | 3 | 8 | 19 | | 2 | 8 | 10 | 19 | 24 | 7 | 19 | 26 | 3 |
| 24 | | 5 | | 2 | | 22 | | 8 | | | | 20 | | 4 |
| 2 | 5 | 26 | 6 | 5 | 16 | 5 | | 16 | 5 | 11 | 3 | 14 | 5 | 8 |
| 19 | | 3 | | 3 | | 8 | | 19 | | 5 | | 10 | | 12 |
| 7 | 25 | 5 | 23 | 6 | 11 | 16 | | 11 | 5 | 23 | 23 | 19 | 15 | 5 |
| 12 | | 24 | | 7 | | 5 | | 26 | | 26 | | 3 | | 17 |

| 1 | 2 | 3 T | 4 | 5 | 6 | 7 | 8 | 9 | 10 | 11 | 12 | 13 |
|---|---|---|---|---|---|---|---|---|---|---|---|---|
| 14 | 15 | 16 | 17 | 18 | 19 A | 20 | 21 | 22 | 23 | 24 | 25 | 26 |

| | | | | | | | | |
|---|---|---|---|---|---|---|---|---|
| 2 | 10 | 10 | 12 | 26 | 25 | 5 | 14 | 20 |

# MYSTERY OBJECT

Add a three-letter word to complete each of the six-letter words below; for example, when the word "ban" is added to "dit", "bandit" is made. When all the words have been completed correctly two words will appear in the shaded squares. These will spell an item of potential value and one Neil MacGregor included in *A History of the World in 100 Objects*.

| | | | | | |
|---|---|---|---|---|---|
| | | | I | O | N |
| | | | P | I | T |
| | | | S | I | T |
| | | | I | C | T |
| | | | W | I | G |
| | | | L | U | S |
| | | | U | A | L |
| | | | I | T | A |
| | | | A | D | E |
| | | | I | T | Y |

# MINI SUDOKU: SUNDAY

Radio 4's *Sunday* offers a look at the ethical and religious issues of the week. In this mini sudoku, complete the grid so that every row, column and 2 × 3 box contains the letters that make up the word "Sunday".

| A |   |   |   | Y |   |
|---|---|---|---|---|---|
|   | N |   |   |   |   |
| Y |   |   |   | U |   |
|   |   |   | N |   |   |
|   |   |   |   |   | U |
| S |   |   | D |   |   |

# MISSING LETTER

Each of the following words is missing a letter. Put the missing letter into the grid below to reveal a programme which was on Radio 4 for over 30 years. What was the programme?

1. S_OCK

2. ST_CK

3. I_EAL

4. S_EET

5. C_ASE

6. _IGHT

7. S_ATE

| M | I | D | W | E | E | K |
|---|---|---|---|---|---|---|
| 1 | 2 | 3 | 4 | 5 | 6 | 7 |

# WORD SEARCH: OLD FAVOURITES

All of the following are programmes once enjoyed on Radio 4, with most now available on Radio 4 Extra. Find them all in the grid.

*After Henry*
*Backrow*
*Checkpoint*
*Does He Take Sugar?*
*Down Your Way*
*Foul Play*
*Frontiers*
*Home Truths*
*Letter from America*
*Listen With Mother*
*Little Britain*

*Many a Slip*
*Masterteam*
*Midweek*
*My Music*
*My Word*
*Petticoat Line*
*Stop the Week*
*Taking Issue*
*The Burkiss Way*
*The Shuttleworths*
*With Great Pleasure*

```
K E R U S A E L P T A E R G H T I W Y
E T H E S H U T T L E W O R T H S X A
E S J U A S T M A E T R E T S A M L C
W P D C Y O H B G K G E K C N V I E I
E V O C H E C K P O I N T I K S S D R
H P W C B E E Y N A Z N A P T R O Q E
T E N F B A C K R O W T G E E E T O M
P T Y U C H J C W W I V N I S V H M A
O T O L B R S N L R O W T H S B E I M
T I U L F P O M B M I N E R P S B D O
S C R T H V A E A T O T F U I H U W R
M O W M T Y L C H R A E U P L T R E F
Y A A Q B T A M F K M I R U S U K E R
W T Y Q T Q O L E A J A I P A R I K E
O L Z I Q T D S P Y U I R S Y T S A T
R I L H H O U L V L T V C A N E S T T
D N S E I G B M Y M U S I C A M W Y E
S E R O A F J R S Q V O D X M O A W L
L U Y R N E H R E T F A F I C H Y I T
```

# NAME BUILDER

The letters of a name have been numbered one to nine. Solve the clues to discover what it is.

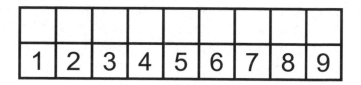

| | | | | | | | | |
|---|---|---|---|---|---|---|---|---|
| 1 | 2 | 3 | 4 | 5 | 6 | 7 | 8 | 9 |

Letters 9, 7, 2 and 1 give us a bellow
Letters 6, 2, 4 and 9 give us something just
Letters 6, 5, 7 and 3 give us sustenance
Letters 2, 8, 3, 4 and 7 give us sound
and letters 3, 5, 8 and 1 give us a grim look
which hopefully the solution will rectify.

# WORD LADDER

*The Goon Show* is one of the classics of radio comedy and is still very much enjoyed on Radio 4 Extra. In this word ladder, take delight in turning, one letter at a time, "Goon" into "Show".

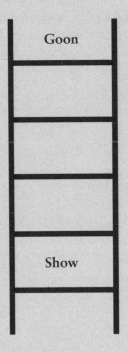

Goon

Show

# CRISS-CROSS: THE WRITE STUFF

Each edition of *The Write Stuff*, which ran from 1998–2014 and was described as a "panel game of literary correctness", featured an author of the week. Some of those featured have been listed below. Now's your chance to see if you have the right stuff by finding places for them in the grid.

**7-letter names**
A. A. Milne
H. G. Wells
T. S. Eliot
W. B. Yeats

**9-letter names**
E. M. Forster
J. K. Rowling
John Donne
Roald Dahl
Ted Hughes

**10-letter names**
Enid Blyton
Ian Fleming
Philip Roth

**11-letter names**
Alan Bennett
Daniel Defoe

**12-letter names**
Anton Chekhov
Harold Pinter
Lewis Carroll

**13-letter name**
Henry Fielding

**14-letter name**
Agatha Christie

# CRYPTOGRAM

Unscramble the cryptogram to discover an amusing observation made by Peter Jones on *Just a Minute*. To give you a start, X = L, G = C, U = R.

| S | P | C | F | S | | ' | C | F | | L | N | Y | | G | N | Z | F | F | Y | X |
|---|---|---|---|---|---|---|---|---|---|---|---|---|---|---|---|---|---|---|---|---|
| | | | | | | | | | | | | | | C | | | | | | L |

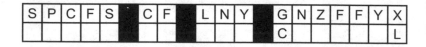

| L | K | F | F | Y | X | | R | P | K | X | J | | H | Y | | X | C | B | Y |
|---|---|---|---|---|---|---|---|---|---|---|---|---|---|---|---|---|---|---|---|
| | | | | | L | | | | | L | | | | | | L | | | |

| Z | W | W | U | P | Z | G | N | C | F | S | | L | N | Y |
|---|---|---|---|---|---|---|---|---|---|---|---|---|---|---|
| | | | R | | | C | | | | | | | | |

| G | P | F | L | C | F | Y | F | L | | C | F | | Z |
|---|---|---|---|---|---|---|---|---|---|---|---|---|---|
| C | | | | | | | | | | | | | |

| V | K | H | T | Z | U | C | F | Y |
|---|---|---|---|---|---|---|---|---|
| | | | | | R | | | |

# MY WORD WORD CHALLENGE

One of the joys of the long-running series *My Word* were rounds in which panellists had to guess the correct meaning of obscure words. Do you know or can you guess the meaning of the following?

1. **Hewgag**
   a) Scarf
   b) Scarecrow or bird scarer
   c) Wooden toy pipe

2. **Paletot**
   a) Sash for tying back curtains
   b) Loose outer coat
   c) Spinning top

3. **Femerall**
   a) A collector of trinkets
   b) An outlet for smoke in a roof
   c) Waste land

4. **Persiflage**
   a) Light-hearted banter
   b) Adage or old country saying
   c) A busybody

# A PICTURE POSER

What former and long-running series is suggested by the following?

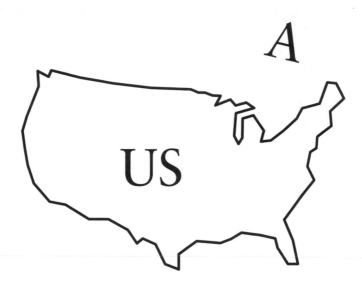

# WHAT THEY SAID

1. In praising the comic talents of Humphrey Lyttelton, scriptwriter Iain Pattinson said. "If you gave him ____ he could read it and make it sound funny." What could he make funny?
   a) Hansard
   b) a telephone directory
   c) the Argos catalogue

2. Writing about *The Archers*, William Smethurst, the programme's editor from 1978–86, stated that "Ambridge is a place…
   a) of dreams, drama and farms."
   b) always slightly nicer than our own."
   c) reflecting the highs and lows of country life."

3. Denis Norden, regular panellist on the long-running series *My Music* said "I'm the resident philistine. I perform comic songs…
   a) in the hope that the lyrics will detract from the fact I can't sing."
   b) to make up for my lack of musical knowledge – and get laughs."
   c) as no one takes my singing seriously."

# MYSTERY ANAGRAMS

Here's a puzzle for those who are long-time listeners to Radio 4 or may enjoy catching up with old recordings on Radio 4 Extra. All the following anagrams are connected by a theme. Can you detect the theme and solve them?

1.  OPEN JESTER

2.  OK, REMIND ME

3.  SMILE WHEN TALKIN'

4.  NO RASCALS IN SHOP

5.  A TIME? – UNJUST

# LETTER DROP

The letters in each of the columns need to be entered into the squares immediately below, but not necessarily in the same order. By placing the letters in the correct places you will reveal the words the *Radio Times* used in 1981 to promote a major serial. What were the words and what is the serial?

| O | D | B | | | | |
|---|---|---|---|---|---|---|
| R | A | I | | | | |
| R | I | B | B | I | G | T | E |
| H | A | O | G | O | T | G | S |
| I | N | N | O | I | O | O | S | D |
| M | H | T | D | B | I | I | O | T |

# STRANGE BUT TRUE

In 1984 the *Kaleidoscope* team used the radio car for the first time. What happened?

a)  During a live broadcast, a policeman opened the door and said the car was causing an obstruction and had to be moved immediately. The policeman was insistent and the broadcast came to a swift conclusion.

b)  The frequency used for the microphones was the same as the frequency being used by a nearby theatre. When the broadcast started, the microphones in the theatre went down.

c)  With it being a live broadcast, there had not been enough time to carry out all the necessary checks. This resulted in an actor rushing from the theatre to give an interview. After a few moments it transpired he was not only a different actor to the one who was meant to be interviewed but was also appearing in a different play.

# MYSTERY SUDOKU

Complete the grid so that every row, column and 3 × 3 box contains the letters ABDEINORY in any order. One row or column contains the eight-letter name of a presenter who contributed much to both Radio 4 and television. Who is it?

| Y |   |   |   | O |   |   | B |   |
|   | D |   | A |   |   | E |   |   |
| O |   | R |   |   |   |   |   | N |
|   |   | A | O |   |   |   |   |   |
| N |   | I |   | B |   | R |   | O |
|   |   |   |   |   | D | A |   |   |
| A |   |   |   |   |   | B |   | D |
|   |   | D |   |   | I |   | R |   |
|   | B |   |   | A |   |   |   | Y |

# CRYPTOGRAM

Solve the cryptogram to discover a parting observation from Jack de Manio, presenter of the *Today* programme from 1958–1971. To give you a start, V = L.

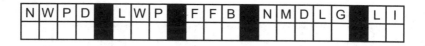

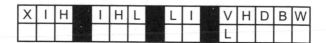

# WORD LADDER

*Last Word* is Radio 4's obituary programme telling the life stories of those who have recently died. With this, the last puzzle in the book, let it be a mark of thanks to all those who have gone before and in some way made a difference. To complete the puzzle, change one letter at a time to turn the word "Last" into "Word".

# ANSWERS

## 1. Anagrams
1. *Gardeners' Question Time*,
2. *Thinking Allowed*, 3. *Great Lives*, 4. *Broadcasting House*,
5. *Desert Island Discs*

## 2. Criss-Cross: Radio 4

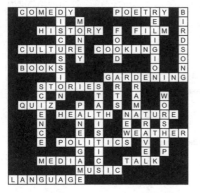

## 3. Trivia
1. Kenneth Williams, 2. Dame Edna Everage, 3. Charlotte Green, 4. Robert Robinson,
5. Sandy, 6. *The Hitchhiker's Guide to the Galaxy*, 7. Uxbridge, 8. *Kaleidoscope*,
9. Sue Perkins, 10. John Ebdon

## 4. Name Builder
Mark Steel

## 5. Mystery Sudoku

| O | I | H | W | M | E | A | D | S |
|---|---|---|---|---|---|---|---|---|
| A | W | S | H | O | D | E | I | M |
| M | E | D | I | A | S | H | O | W |
| W | H | M | D | E | I | O | S | A |
| I | S | A | O | H | W | D | M | E |
| D | O | E | M | S | A | I | W | H |
| H | M | W | A | D | O | S | E | I |
| S | A | O | E | I | M | W | H | D |
| E | D | I | S | W | H | M | A | O |

## 6. *The Now Show* – Phobias
1b, 2a, 3a, 4c

## 7. Odd One Out
The letter R. This is the only letter that touches the box in three places.

## 8. Cryptogram
"It is impossible, after listening to great music, to write absolute rubbish."

### 9. Word Search:
*Today* Presenters

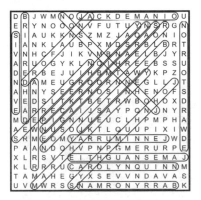

### 10. Coded Crossword

*Farming Today* announced that "giraffe milk" would go on sale

### 11. True or False?
1. False. Harold Wilson never appeared on *Desert Island Discs*, 2. True, 3. False, 4. True, 5. True. There had been a mix up over who read certain lines in the script, 6. False, 7. True, 8. False

### 12. Programme Builder
*Soul Music*

### 13. Missing Letters
1. *I'm Sorry I Haven't a Clue*, 2. *In Our Time*, 3. *The Unbelievable Truth*, 4. *Tweet of the Day*, 5. *More or Less*, 6. *Dead Ringers*, 7. *In Touch*, 8. *Law in Action*, 9. *Analysis*, 10. *A Good Read*

### 14. Desert Island Luxury
1f, 2d (especially one that made rum and raisin ice cream!), 3e, 4a, 5b, 6c

### 15. Anagrams
1. Anne Swithinbank, 2. Bob Flowerdew, 3. Matthew Wilson, 4. Christine Walkden, 5. Pippa Greenwood

### 16. Word Search:
*The Life Scientific*

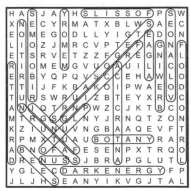

## 17. Mini Sudoku: Studio

| I | O | D | S | U | T |
|---|---|---|---|---|---|
| S | U | T | D | O | I |
| D | S | I | U | T | O |
| U | T | O | I | D | S |
| T | D | S | O | I | U |
| O | I | U | T | S | D |

## 18. A Picture Poser
*Inside Science*

## 19. Cryptogram
"A good new pair of secateurs or jam from the garden's fruits and chillies."

## 20. On Track
Russell Davies, Nigel Rees, David Mitchell and Paul Gambaccini

## 21. Crossword

## 22. Letter Drop
"Our approach is invariably sceptical, but always fair."

## 23. Presenters
1g, 2h, 3j, 4i, 5f, 6a, 7b, 8d, 9c, 10e

## 24. Word Ladder
One possible solution: long, song, sang, sane, save, wave

## 25. Coded Crossword

The book was *Puckoon*, written by Spike Milligan.

## 26. Mystery Sudoku

| A | H | L | R | I | M | G | E | T |
|---|---|---|---|---|---|---|---|---|
| G | E | T | L | H | A | R | M | I |
| I | R | M | E | G | T | L | H | A |
| H | T | G | I | A | L | E | R | M |
| E | I | R | T | M | G | H | A | L |
| L | M | A | H | E | R | I | T | G |
| R | L | H | A | T | I | M | G | E |
| T | G | E | M | L | H | A | I | R |
| M | A | I | G | R | E | T | L | H |

## 27. A Picture Poser
*Costing* (cost tin) *the Earth*

## 28. Anagrams
1. *Tweet of the Day*, 2. *Green Originals*, 3. *Nature Table*, 4. *Ramblings*, 5. *Open Country*

## 29. What They Said
1c, 2a, 3b

## 30. Strange but True
c) A recording of the previous Boxing Day's *Thought for the Day* was played by mistake. Following this, it resulted in *Thought for the Day* being broadcast live so that the talks would be more topical.

## 31. Programme Jig
*Desert Island Discs, Today, Gardeners' Question Time, Great Lives, In Touch*

## 32. Criss-Cross:
*The Bottom Line*

## 33. Cryptogram
"Six foot boa constrictor. Free to a good home. Very friendly, good eater, likes children."

## 34. Letter Drop
"An essential service in the life of the nation."

## 35. Word Search: Programmes

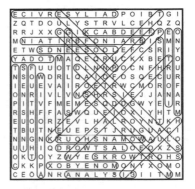

## 36. Cross Out
WORMS; worms have often been praised by the *Gardeners' Question Time* panel as "nature's helpers", particularly in the way they condition and aerate the soil.

## 37. Mystery Sudoku

| R | C | S | L | A | O | K | M | E |
| K | M | L | R | E | C | S | A | O |
| O | A | E | K | S | M | C | R | L |
| C | R | A | O | M | E | L | K | S |
| L | O | M | A | K | S | E | C | R |
| E | S | K | C | R | L | A | O | M |
| A | E | O | S | C | R | M | L | K |
| S | K | R | M | L | A | O | E | C |
| M | L | C | E | O | K | R | S | A |

## 38. A Picture Poser
*Archive* (ark hive) *on 4*

### 39. Anagrams
1. Chris Aldridge, 2. Kathy Clugston, 3. Zeb Soanes, 4. Alan Smith, 5. Susan Rae

### 40. Programme Builder
*In Our Time*

### 41. Take Your Pick
1b, 2c, 3a

### 42. On Track
*Ed Reardon's Week, More or Less, Inside Science, Beyond Belief*

### 43. Word Ladder
One possible solution: life, like, lake, fake, fare, farm

### 44. Acrostics
1. Pillow, 2. Enough, 3. Tahiti, 4. Expect, 5. Riddle. The letters in the shaded squares spell Peter White

### 45. Strange but True
c) The recording sounded as if it had come from *The Goon Show*. It was such a short piece that Charlotte and several of her colleagues did not have enough time to recover their composure. The piece and accompanying laughter was much appreciated by the *Today* audience and played again later in the programme.

### 46. Mini Sudoku: Script

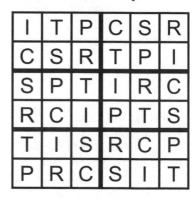

| I | T | P | C | S | R |
|---|---|---|---|---|---|
| C | S | R | T | P | I |
| S | P | T | I | R | C |
| R | C | I | P | T | S |
| T | I | S | R | C | P |
| P | R | C | S | I | T |

### 47. A Picture Poser
Pieces of Eight. The figure eight is in eight pieces.

### 48. Word Search: *Inside Health*

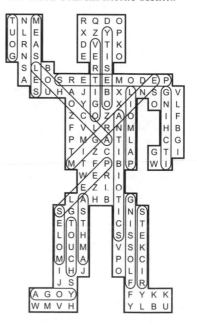

**49. Crossword**

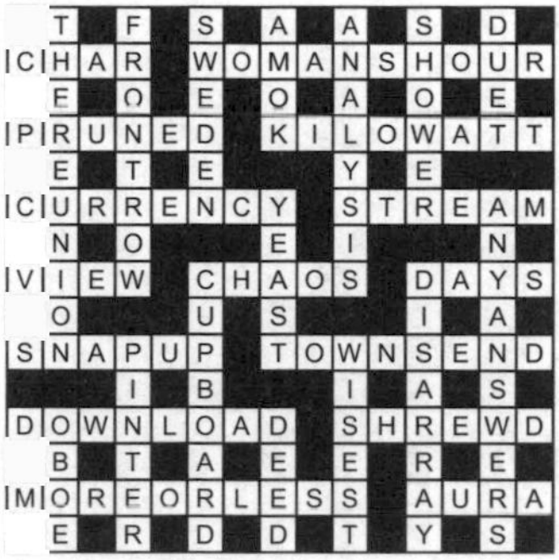

**50. Name Builder**
Ed Reardon

**51. Letter Drop**
"I loved the idea of taking the listeners by surprise with unlikely juxtapositions."

**52. Word Search:**
***The Living World***

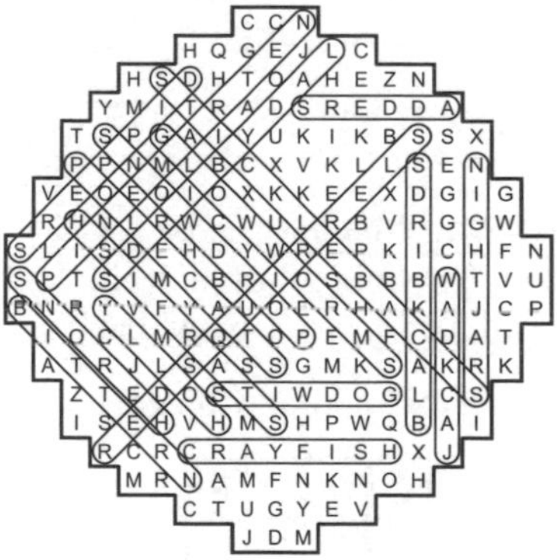

**53. Anagrams**
1. Paul Merton, 2. Gyles Brandreth, 3. Sue Perkins, 4. Tony Hawks, 5. Sheila Hancock

**54. Strange but True**
a) Listeners sent in a great many versions and renditions of the *Upstairs, Downstairs* theme tune, including one by the celebrated composer John Tavener. A CD containing pieces sent in by listeners was released in 2010 in aid of Children in Need.

**55. Word Search:**
**Mornington Crescent**

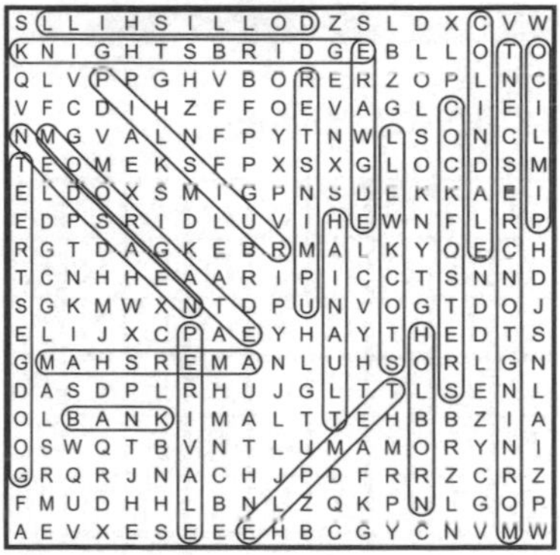

**56. Inside *Inside Science***
The topics need to be entered in the following order: Ozone Hole, Drones, GM Plants, Fatty Food, Penguins, Solar Farm, Narwhals, Dark Matter, Cold Snap. The word formed in the shaded square and another subject *Inside Science* has explored is Holograms.

## 57. Criss-Cross: *Book at Bedtime*

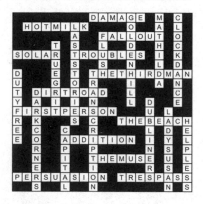

## 58. Mystery Sudoku

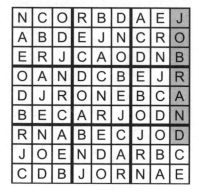

## 59. Anagrams
1. Susan Powell, 2. Tomasz Schafernaker, 3. Chris Fawkes, 4. Matt Taylor, 5. Helen Willetts

## 60. Tuning In
*Soul Music, Front Row, Great Lives*

## 61. Coded Crossword

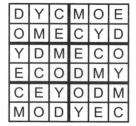

The something helpful is "BBC Sounds", the streaming media and audio download service from the BBC.

## 62. Programme Jig
*The Unbelievable Truth, Loose Ends, Analysis, Farming Today, Woman's Hour*

## 63. Museum Donations
1c, 2d, 3e, 4a, 5b

## 64. Cross Out
*News Quiz*

## 65. Word Ladder
One possible solution: feed, fend, bend, band, bank, back

## 66. Mini Sudoku: Comedy

| D | Y | C | M | O | E |
|---|---|---|---|---|---|
| O | M | E | C | Y | D |
| Y | D | M | E | C | O |
| E | C | O | D | M | Y |
| C | E | Y | O | D | M |
| M | O | D | Y | E | C |

## 67. A Picture Poser
*File on 4*

## 68. On Track
Pam Ayres, Sarah Millican, Jenny Eclair, Jo Brand, Sue Perkins

## 69. Anagrams
1. Sherlock Holmes, 2. Hercule Poirot, 3. Charles Paris, 4. Miss Marple, 5. Maigret

## 70. Mystery Sudoku

| H | I | K | C | T | N | U | L | O |
|---|---|---|---|---|---|---|---|---|
| O | N | C | U | L | H | T | K | I |
| U | T | L | I | K | O | N | C | H |
| K | O | N | T | H | L | C | I | U |
| I | U | H | N | O | C | L | T | K |
| L | C | T | K | I | U | O | H | N |
| T | H | U | L | N | I | K | O | C |
| C | L | I | O | U | K | H | N | T |
| N | K | O | H | C | T | I | U | L |

## 71. Strange but True
c)

## 72. Criss-Cross: *Just a Minute*

## 73. Mystery Track
*The Hitchhiker's Guide to the Galaxy*

## 74. Mystery Word
The word in the shaded squares is "trailer", and with the missing three-letter words being: ate, era, cab, lit, all, net, are

## 75. Letter Drop
"It's a rural idyll in which secretly we would all like to live."

## 76. Anagrams
1. Sarah Montague, 2. Martha Kearney, 3. Carolyn Quinn, 4. Laura Kuenssberg, 5. Chris Mason

## 77. Trivia
1. *The Patch*, 2. North Wales, 3. Milton Jones, 4. *The Listening Project*, 5. Writer, 6. Libby Purves, 7. Eddie Mair, 8. The Reverend Geraldine Granger was none other than Dawn French in character as the fictional Vicar of Dibley. This *Thought for the Day* special was part of Radio 4's Character Invasion Day, 9. Timewasting, 10. His imaginary sandwich bar

## 78. A Picture Poser
*The Bottom Line*

## 79. Take Your Pick
1b, 2b, 3b

## 80. Programme Jig
*Feedback, Broadcasting House, Start the Week, Beyond Belief, Four Thought*

## 81. Acrostics
1. Scheme, 2. Thread, 3. Artist, 4. Mirror, 5. Assent. The name in the shaded squares is Chris Mason.

## 82. Mystery Sudoku

| R | E | L | M | I | F | V | O | G |
|---|---|---|---|---|---|---|---|---|
| F | I | G | L | O | V | E | R | M |
| V | O | M | E | R | G | F | I | L |
| I | L | E | F | V | O | M | G | R |
| G | M | V | R | E | L | I | F | O |
| O | R | F | I | G | M | L | V | E |
| E | F | I | G | M | R | O | L | V |
| L | V | R | O | F | E | G | M | I |
| M | G | O | V | L | I | R | E | F |

## 83. Criss-Cross: *Ramblings*

## 84. Desert Island Luxury
1c, 2f, 3a, 4b, 5d, 6e

## 85. Word Ladder
One possible solution is: book, boot, bout, gout, glut, glue, clue, club

## 86. Mystery Series
The words need to be entered in the following order: sketch, midday, strobe, éclair, throne, review and Inuits. The series that appears in the shaded squares is *Kitchen Cabinet*.

## 87. Cryptogram
"I notice from the sheer weight of this week's postbag, we've received a little over no letters."

## 88. Word Search: *The Archers*

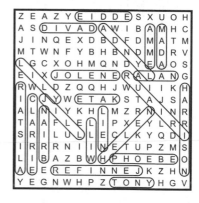

## 89. Crossword

| | S | | S | | S | | I | | A | | S | | S |
|---|---|---|---|---|---|---|---|---|---|---|---|---|---|
| R | E | P | E | A | T | | M | O | N | E | Y | B | O | X |
| | M | | L | | R | P | | Y | | M | | N |
| D | O | V | E | T | A | I | L | | H | U | B | C | A | P |
| | L | | C | | D | O | | O | | O | | T |
| G | I | F | T | E | D | | D | O | W | N | L | O | A | D |
| | N | | | | L | E | | E | | | I |
| J | A | C | K | D | E | E | | O | F | F | C | U | T | S |
| | | A | | | S | | E | | | R |
| F | R | O | N | T | R | O | W | | E | Y | E | L | I | D |
| | A | | G | | E | | E | | D | | D | | G |
| S | C | R | A | W | L | | A | M | B | R | I | D | G | E |
| | I | | R | E | T | | A | | T | | E |
| A | N | N | O | U | N | C | E | | C | H | O | I | R | S |
| | G | | O | | T | | R | | K | | R | | S |

## 90. Programme Builder
*Life Lines*. This was the winner for the Best Original Series or Serial at the BBC Audio Drama Awards 2020.

## 91. U-pun *My Word*
1. Maybe It's Because I'm a Londoner, 2. Show Me The Way To Go Home, 3. Hope springs eternal in the human breast, 4. He who hesitates is lost, 5. I'm Dreaming of a White Christmas, 6. Around the World in Eighty Days, 7. Too many cooks spoil the broth, 8. Charity begins at home

## 92. Anagrams
1. Paul Gambaccini, 2. Roger Bolton, 3. Matthew Parris, 4. Richard Coles, 5. Mark Coles

## 93. A Picture Poser
*Short Works*

## 94. Hidden Places
1. Corby, 2. Bedford, 3. Leith, 4. Wigan, 5. Dartford, 6. Boston

## 95. A Riddle
*Today*

## 96. Criss-Cross:
*The Food Programme*

## 97. Word Search: Radio 4

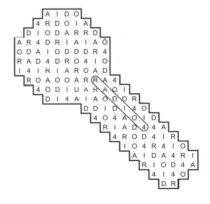

## 98. Mini Sudoku: Acting

| A | G | T | C | I | N |
|---|---|---|---|---|---|
| C | I | N | G | T | A |
| I | C | A | N | G | T |
| T | N | G | I | A | C |
| G | A | C | T | N | I |
| N | T | I | A | C | G |

## 99. Anagrams
1. Pam Ayres, 2. Tim Vine,
3. Mark Steel, 4. Sandi Toksvig,
5. Graeme Garden

## 100. A Timely Puzzle
The words need to be entered
in the following order: ballad,
midday, engine, stable, spider,
action. The "something familiar"
that appears in the shaded
squares is Big Ben – a timely
puzzle indeed!

## 101. Word Ladder
One possible solution: good,
gold, told, toll, tall, talk, walk

## 102. Cross Out
*Mr Pye*

## 103. Take Your Pick
1c, 2a, 3c

## 104. Mystery Sudoku

| U | D | I | A | N | M | G | Y | R |
|---|---|---|---|---|---|---|---|---|
| Y | M | G | D | U | R | I | A | N |
| A | R | N | Y | G | I | U | M | D |
| R | G | Y | U | D | A | M | N | I |
| N | U | D | I | M | G | Y | R | A |
| I | A | M | R | Y | N | D | G | U |
| D | N | R | M | I | Y | A | U | G |
| M | I | A | G | R | U | N | D | Y |
| G | Y | U | N | A | D | R | I | M |

Mia Grundy is a character in
*The Archers*.

## 105. Word Search: *Poetry Please*

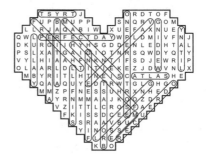

## 106. Curious Titles
1c, 2a, 3c

## 107. Programme Jig
*Sunday Worship, The Life
Scientific, Open Country,
Bookclub, Thinking Allowed*

## 108. Criss-Cross:
### Gardeners' Question Time

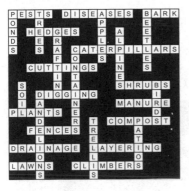

## 109. Presenters
1i, 2g, 3e, 4b, 5c, 6j, 7a, 8d, 9f, 10h

## 110. A Picture Poser
*Beyond Belief.* Bee on B. Leaf

## 111. Word Quest
The word that has relevance to Radio 4 and uses all the letters is "broadcast". Some of the other words that can be made are: abator, aboard, abort, abroad, acrobat, actor, adsorb, aorta, arco, boar, board, boart, boat, bora, bort, broad, card, carob, castor, coast, coat, cobra, coda, cord, cost, costa, costard, doat, dost, oast, octad, orca, rabato, road, roast, rota, sabot, scot, soar, soda, sora, sorb, sord, sort, stoa, stob, tabor, taco, taro, toad, torc, trod

## 112. Take Your Pick
1c, 2b, 3c

## 113. Mystery Sudoku

## 114. What They Said
1c, 2a, 3b

## 115. Coded Crossword

The definition of "lactic" according to the dictionary used in *I'm Sorry I Haven't a Clue* is "A stopped clock".

## 116. Anagrams
1. Clare Balding, 2. Miles Jupp, 3. Winifred Robinson, 4. Michael Rosen, 5. Laurie Taylor

## 117. Name Builder
Neil Sleat

## 118. Mini Sudoku: Listen

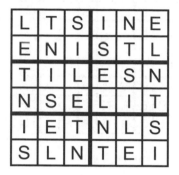

| L | T | S | I | N | E |
|---|---|---|---|---|---|
| E | N | I | S | T | L |
| T | I | L | E | S | N |
| N | S | E | L | I | T |
| I | E | T | N | L | S |
| S | L | N | T | E | I |

## 119. One From the Other
1. *A Good Read, Poetry Please*,
2. *Broadcasting House, Saturday Review*

## 120. Cryptogram
"The *World at One* was actually the start of modern-day broadcast current affairs."

## 121. Word Search: Weekend Programmes

## 122. Reith Lectures
1d, 2f, 3a, 4h, 5b, 6g, 7c, 8e

## 123. Letter Drop
"Excuse me. Did you see where I left my hat?"

## 124. Crossword

| | | A | C | S | U | I | | |
| B | A | L | L | A | S | T | M E D I A | |
... (grid)

## 125. Programme Jig
*Short Works, The Media Show, Round Britain Quiz, Soul Music, Ramblings*

## 126. Anagrams
1. Adam Rutherford, 2. James Naughtie, 3. Andrew Marr, 4. Sheila Dillon, 5. Paul Lewis

## 127. Acrostics
1. Right, 2. Alibi, 3. Dream, 4. Image, 5. Oasis. The shaded squares spell "*Radio Times*".

## 128. Trivia
1. The Law, 2. Mark Watson, 3. Jonathan Dimbleby, 4. *Broadcasting House*,

5. 1.45 p.m., 6. "The answer lies in the soil", 7. "By the Sleepy Lagoon", 8. *Tales from the Stave*, 9. Tom Vernon, 10. *I'm Sorry I Haven't a Clue*

### 129. Strange but True
b) Evan Davis thought he was talking to Robert Shapiro, the former lawyer to OJ Simpson. Instead he ended up talking to Robert Shapiro, an advisor to Democratic presidents.

### 130. Mystery Feature
Slow radio

### 131. Letter Drop
"Reflections from a faith perspective on issues and people in the news." This refers to *Thought for the Day.*

### 132. Mystery Sudoku

| O | T | D | N | U | E | B | I | S |
|---|---|---|---|---|---|---|---|---|
| S | U | B | I | D | T | N | E | O |
| N | I | E | O | S | B | T | D | U |
| U | E | T | D | B | I | S | O | N |
| I | B | O | U | N | S | E | T | D |
| D | S | N | T | E | O | I | U | B |
| E | N | U | S | T | D | O | B | I |
| B | O | S | E | I | U | D | N | T |
| T | D | I | B | O | N | U | S | E |

### 133. Desert Island Luxury
1e, 2a, 3f, 4b, 5d, 6c

### 134. Mystery Poem
The poems need to be entered in the following order from top to bottom: *Thistles, Winter, October, Heatwave, Digging, Weathers, Soracte* and *Postscript.* The poem title created in the shaded squares is *Snowdrop.*

### 135. Cryptogram
"Getting to the heart of country life with a look at individual farming endeavours." (This is the objective of *On Your Farm.*)

### 136. *Quote... Unquote*
1. Groucho Marx, 2. Johann Wolfgang Goethe, 3. George Bernard Shaw, 4. Ralph Waldo Emerson, 5. Douglas Adams

### 137. Archers Trivia
1. Barwick Green, 2. Jazzer's tarantula, 3. Freddie Pargetter, 4. Jim Lloyd, 5. St Stephen's and the vicar is Alan Franks, 6. Eccles, and Kenton accidentally hit it, 7. Rob Titchener, her husband at the time, 8. Nigel Pargetter, 9. The B at Ambridge, 10. Duchess of Cornwall

### 138. Anagrams
1. *I'm Sorry I Haven't a Clue,* 2. *The Now Show,* 3. *The Unbelievable Truth,* 4. *Dead Ringers,* 5. *Ed Reardon's Week*

## 139. Coded Crossword

| | B | A | | S | F | | C | A | | S |
|---|---|---|---|---|---|---|---|---|---|---|
| P | U | N | T | | T | H | E | N | O | W | S | H | O | W |
| | C | T | | A | | T | M | | S | N |
| S | K | I | I | N | G | | A | M | B | R | I | D | G | E |
| | L | T | | E | | | | Z | | |
| P | E | R | U | | H | A | R | D | C | H | E | E | S | E |
| | D | D | | A | | A | O | | | T |
| D | O | Z | E | | N | I | N | T | H | | A | J | A | R |
| | W | | | D | | G | E | | C | T |
| A | N | Y | A | N | S | W | E | R | S | | C | R | U | X |
| | | V | | | I | | | O | | E |
| C | I | T | I | Z | E | N | S | | V | A | L | I | S | E |
| | N | A | | M | | A | E | | A | Q |
| U | N | F | R | U | I | T | F | U | L | | D | O | U | R |
| | S | Y | | T | E | | Y | | E | E |

The person often heard on Radio 4 is Helen Archer.

## 140. Who Is It?
1. Peter Gibbs, 2. Martha Kearney, 3. Frances Fyfield, 4. Simon Brett, 5. Ian Messiter

## 141. Anagrams
1. Neil Sleat, 2. Charles Carroll, 3. Corrie Corfield, 4. Caroline Nicholls, 5. Diana Speed

## 142. Mystery Sudoku

| V | A | T | E | C | I | H | M | R |
|---|---|---|---|---|---|---|---|---|
| I | M | H | A | T | R | C | E | V |
| R | C | E | V | H | M | A | I | T |
| T | V | A | I | E | H | M | R | C |
| E | I | M | R | V | C | T | A | H |
| C | H | R | T | M | A | I | V | E |
| A | R | C | H | I | V | E | T | M |
| M | T | V | C | A | E | R | H | I |
| H | E | I | M | R | T | V | C | A |

## 143. Between the Lines
*In Touch*

## 144. Strange but True
c) Nicholas noted that another contestant had deviated and, as Pam was new to the game, he urged her to press her buzzer and get in with a challenge. Pam was still unsure so Nicholas took the unusual step of getting up and pressing the buzzer for her.

## 145. A Picture Poser
*More or Less*

## 146. Word Ladder
One possible solution: smart, start, stare, store, stone, shone, phone

## 147. Criss-Cross: *In Our Time*

## 148. Timeline
1h, 2f, 3g, 4i, 5c (This was on the Midland Region. *The Archers* made its national debut in 1951), 6d, 7b, 8e, 9a

## 149. Mystery Sudoku

| L | R | S | A | M | I | B | N | G |
|---|---|---|---|---|---|---|---|---|
| N | A | I | L | G | B | R | M | S |
| B | M | G | N | S | R | L | A | I |
| S | B | N | M | I | G | A | R | L |
| M | L | A | R | N | S | G | I | B |
| G | I | R | B | L | A | M | S | N |
| I | N | M | G | R | L | S | B | A |
| R | G | B | S | A | N | I | L | M |
| A | S | L | I | B | M | N | G | R |

## 150. Museum Donations
1e, 2a, 3d, 4c, 5b

## 151. Trivia
1. *Letter from America*, 2. *The Briefing Room*, 3. *The Goon Show*, 4. The pips, 5. The cricket commentator Christopher Martin Jenkins, 6. Charles Paris, 7. Nigeria, 8. Peter Jones, 9. The foot-and-mouth disease crisis, 10. Ed Reardon

## 152. The *Today* Challenge
Scrambled egg

## 153. Tuning In
*Open Country, Any Answers, Sunday*

## 154. Word Search:
### *Shipping Forecast*

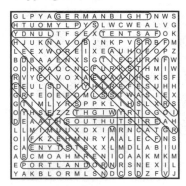

## 155. Mini Sudoku: Grundy

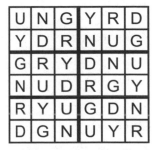

| U | N | G | Y | R | D |
|---|---|---|---|---|---|
| Y | D | R | N | U | G |
| G | R | Y | D | N | U |
| N | U | D | R | G | Y |
| R | Y | U | G | D | N |
| D | G | N | U | Y | R |

## 156. Top Five
The winner of the poll was *Desert Island Discs*, *The Archers* was second followed by *Round the Horne*, *Hancock's Half Hour* and *In The Psychiatrist's Chair*.

## 157. Anagrams
1. Marcus Brigstocke, 2. Hugh Dennis, 3. Milton Jones, 4. Steve Punt, 5. Barry Cryer

## 158. Cross Out
Rumpole of the Bailey

## 159. Criss-Cross: *Tweet of the Day*

## 160. Take Your Pick
1c, 2b, 3a

## 161. A Picture Poser
*Crossing Continents*

## 162. Heard at Ambridge?
1c, 2b, 3a, 4c

## 163. Coded Crossword

| Q |   | S |   | O |   | C | U |   | A |   | A |
|---|---|---|---|---|---|---|---|---|---|---|---|
| U | N | I | Q | U | O | T | E |   | O | M | N | I | B | U | S |
| E |   | U |   | O |   | D |   | W |   | D |   | S |   | H |
| B | R | I | I | S | T | L | E |   | O | V | E | R | E | A | T |
| E |   | R |   |   | M |   | R |   | F |   | N |   | R |
| C | H | E | A | P | J | A | C | K |   | E | X | T | R | A |
|   |   | R |   |   | E |   | A |   | E |   | Y |
| E | X | P | L | O | D | E |   | R | O | T | T | E | R | S |
| U |   | A |   | G |   | M |   |   | E |
| R | O | V | E | R |   | B | R | O | A | D | C | A | S | T |
| Y |   | I |   | A |   | L |   | X |   | C |   | I |
| D | I | I | L | E | M | M | A |   | Y | O | G | H | U | R | T |
| I |   | I |   | M |   | Z |   | G |   | A |   | M |   | L |
| C | I | L | O | S | E | T | O |   | E | X | T | R | E | M | E |
| E |   | N |   | S |   | N |   | N |   | E |   | N |   | D |

It is 'the pips' that are often heard on Radio 4.

## 164. Mystery Sudoku

| T | H | I | B | N | R | A | C | E |
|---|---|---|---|---|---|---|---|---|
| E | R | B | C | T | A | N | I | H |
| A | N | C | I | E | H | B | T | R |
| I | B | E | A | R | T | C | H | N |
| R | A | H | E | C | N | T | B | I |
| N | C | T | H | B | I | R | E | A |
| B | E | N | R | I | C | H | A | T |
| C | T | A | N | H | E | I | R | B |
| H | I | R | T | A | B | E | N | C |

## 165. A Puzzling Poser
The person was listening to the radio in a car. As they drove through a tunnel, radio reception was lost.

## 166. *The Moral Maze*

## 167. X
The words need to be entered into the following order: Impish, answer, mosaic, belief, steady, handle. The series which appears in the shaded squares is *Inside Health*.

**168. Anagrams**
1. *The Archers*, 2. *In Their Element*, 3. *Four Thought*, 4. *The Kitchen Cabinet*, 5. *Word of Mouth*

**169. Programme Builder**
*A Good Read*

**170. Word Search: *Soul Music***

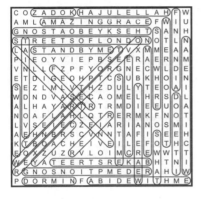

**171. Word Ladder**
One possible solution: news, sews, sees, seem, stem, item

**172. Riddle**
Appeal

**173. Strange but True**
b)

**174. A Picture Poser**
*All in the Mind*

**175. Word Search: *Woman's Hour***

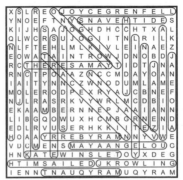

**176. What They Said**
1a, 2b, 3b

**177. Trivia**
1. Fags and Mags, 2. Michael Parkinson, 3. Diagnosis, 4. *Gardeners' Question Time*, 5. Stephen Fry, 6. Dr Anthony Clare, 7. Paul Temple, 8. Richard Coles, 9. *Only Artists*, 10. *The Infinite Monkey Cage*

**178. Criss-Cross: *The Digital Human***

## 179. On Track
Sheila Dillon, Justin Webb, Jenni Murray, Winifred Robinson

## 180. Letter Drop
"How horse manure helped Victorians have pineapples."

## 181. Cryptogram
"Anyone who's too slow to get out of the way, basically."

## 182. *Round Britain Quiz*
1. Aberdeen, 2. Severn,
3. Staffordshire, 4. Bakerloo,
5. Red Lion, 6. Isle of Wight,
7. Hay-on-Wye, 8. Douglas,
9. Alfred Wainwright, 10. York

## 183. Coded Crossword

| G | M |   | S |   | A |   | S |   | J |   | V |   | S |
|---|---|---|---|---|---|---|---|---|---|---|---|---|---|
| A | Q | U | A | T | I | C |   | U | R | A | N | I | U | M |
| Z |   | E |   | I |   | C |   | R |   | C |   | G |   | A |
| U | P | S | U | R | G | E |   | V | I | K | I | N | G | S |
| M |   | L |   |   | D |   | E |   | K |   | E |   | H |
| P | R | I | V | A | T | E | L | Y |   | N | O | T | C | H |
|   |   | L |   |   | O |   | I |   | T |   | I |
| F | A | U | X | P | A | S |   | R | E | F | L | E | C | T |
| E | N |   | H | U |   | E |   |   |   |   | E |
| E | X | I | T | R | A |   | B | R | O | A | D | C | A | S | T |
| D |   | E |   | B |   | M |   | R |   |   | F |   | U |
| B | E | S | I | E | G | E |   | G | E | N | T | L | E | R |
| A |   | T |   | T |   | R |   | A |   | E |   | O |   | K |
| C | H | E | W | I | N | G |   | N | E | W | W | A | V | E |
| K |   | D |   | C |   | E |   | S |   | S |   | T |   | Y |

The something to listen to and own was "Bookshelf". *Bookshelf* was a literary series which ran from 1978–1993 with some editions still available to hear.

## 184. Mystery Object
The three-letter words that need to be entered into the grid are act, arm, bed, add, big, sty, act, cap, arc and odd. The two words formed in the shaded squares spelling an item of potential value are "credit card".

## 185. Mini Sudoku: *Sunday*

| A | S | D | U | Y | N |
|---|---|---|---|---|---|
| U | N | Y | A | D | S |
| Y | A | N | S | U | D |
| D | U | S | N | A | Y |
| N | D | A | Y | S | U |
| S | Y | U | D | N | A |

## 186. Missing Letter
*Midweek*

## 187. Word Search:
Old Favourites

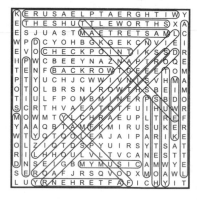

## 188. Name Builder
Radio Four

## 189. Word Ladder
One possible solution: goon, soon, soot, shot, show

## 190. Criss-Cross:
### The Write Stuff

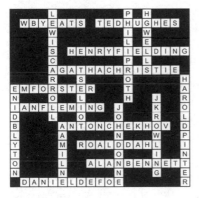

## 191. Cryptogram
"Going in the Channel Tunnel would be like approaching the Continent in a submarine."

## 192. My Word Word Challenge
1c, 2b, 3b, 4a

## 193. A Picture Poser
*Letter from America*

## 194. What They Said
1c, 2b, 3a

## 195. Mystery Anagrams
1. Peter Jones, 2. Derek Nimmo, 3. Kenneth Williams, 4. Nicholas Parsons, 5. *Just a Minute* –

and this is the theme and link between them all.

## 196. Letter Drop
"Radio is Hobbit 4 ming. Get into good Radio 4 hobbits." These were the words on badges produced by the *Radio Times* to promote *The Lord of the Rings*. It was also one of the first Radio 4 programmes to be transmitted in stereo.

## 197. Strange but True
b)

## 198. Mystery Sudoku

| Y | A | E | R | O | N | D | B | I |
|---|---|---|---|---|---|---|---|---|
| B | D | N | A | I | Y | E | O | R |
| O | I | R | E | D | B | Y | A | N |
| D | Y | A | O | R | E | I | N | B |
| N | E | I | Y | B | A | R | D | O |
| R | O | B | I | N | D | A | Y | E |
| A | R | Y | N | E | O | B | I | D |
| E | N | D | B | Y | I | O | R | A |
| I | B | O | D | A | R | N | E | Y |

## 199. Cryptogram
"When the BBC wants to sack you, they take you out to lunch."

## 200. Word Ladder
One possible solution: last, lost, post, port, pork, work, word

# ACKNOWLEDGEMENTS

This book has been a great delight to compile and I would like to start by thanking all at Radio 4 and the BBC for what they do and the service they give.

My thanks as always to my wife Ros and my son and daughter, Richard and Emily, for their support and input. The team at Summersdale have also been wonderful to work with and I would particularly like to thank my editor, Claire Berrisford, as well as Chris Stone, Neil Kelly and Claire Plimmer.

Thanks also go to David Finnerty for gamely tackling some of the puzzles and his technical expertise, and to Mary Pooley and Michael Beasley.

Last but not least, my thanks to you, the reader, for your interest and support. It is you that makes this so very worthwhile.

# ABOUT THE AUTHOR

**Neil Somerville** has had a long association with the BBC, working at the BBC Written Archives Centre for over 20 years. It was in this position that he was able to delve into BBC history as well as provide research for a variety of programmes. During this time he also compiled trivia for the *Radio Times* and puzzle books for and about the BBC.

In addition, Neil has written and compiled many bestselling books including *For the Love of The Archers: The Unofficial Puzzle Book*, *Cat Wisdom: 60 Great Lessons You Can Learn from a Cat*, a long-running series on Chinese horoscopes as well as many other popular puzzle books, notably *The Literary Pocket Puzzle Book* and *The British Puzzle Book*. He also contributes to newspapers and magazines and has compiled puzzles for *The Countryman* magazine for many years.

Neil lives in Berkshire with his wife, has two adult children, is a keen walker and enjoys being out in the countryside. His website is www.neilsomerville.com

If you're interested in finding out more about our books, find us on Facebook at **Summersdale Publishers** and follow us on Twitter at **@Summersdale**

# www.summersdale.com

## Image Credits